THE
UNITED STATES AND CANADA

Teaching Resources

WORLD EXPLORER

PRENTICE HALL

Prentice
Hall

Needham, Massachusetts
Upper Saddle River, New Jersey
Glenview, Illinois

Section Reading Support Transparencies

A Section Reading Support Transparency is provided for each section of the textbook. Each Section Reading Support Transparency provides a graphic organizer framework to help guide students in answering the Questions to Explore that begin each section. You may also use these transparencies to preview or review sections as you teach them.

Graphic organizers are classroom-tested learning tools to help you think key process of information in a visual summary. The shape of the organizer show relationships between the pieces of information. Graphic organizers are especially useful to visual learners.

Each graphic organizer in this transparency system represents a reading skill that requires a critical thinking skill. You can reinforce the thinking skill as you show the graphic organizer.

Venn Diagram	The overlapping circles of a Venn diagram are useful for comparing and contrasting similarities and differences.
Flow Chart	The linear presentation of a time line helps students see a chronological sequence of events.
Cycle Chart	A cycle chart represents a sequence of events that occur in a process, or a series of related events.
Concept Web	The linear graphic concept web contains the main idea in the center surrounded by details or the supporting details.
Class Table	The elements of a table include a classification of components.
Outline	An outline shows the main ideas in a section based on the way the section is structured, plus the details that support the main ideas in details and references.
Cause/Effect Chart	Whether showing a cause because a chain or a study of chains of causes or effects, the chart format makes clear the cause and effect connection between events and outcomes.

LETTER HOME

CHAPTER 1

THE UNITED STATES AND CANADA
Physical Geography

Social Studies Hot Line

Dear Family,

For the next few weeks, our social studies class will be studying the United States and Canada. We will be looking at the geography, history, and cultures of our nation and our northern neighbor. As we progress through the text, I hope that you will offer your child any insights or information that you may have on the different topics we explore.

In Chapter 1, we will study the land, water, climate, vegetation, and natural resources of the United States and Canada. As your child looks at the maps in this chapter, you might encourage him or her to identify our area's climate, vegetation, natural resources, and outstanding landforms.

Ask your child questions such as "Are there large rivers or other bodies of water nearby? What is the climate like here? At what elevation do we live? At what latitude? How does our location compare with other places, such as Edmonton, Alberta; Phoenix, Arizona; or Honolulu, Hawaii?" Traveling through the area surrounding our community may also give you a good opportunity to discuss the geography of the region with your child.

You might also watch the news with your child and listen for reports about environmental issues and natural resources. Help your child look for interesting newspaper or magazine articles about debates over the use of natural resources, such as trees, minerals, and water.

In the weeks ahead, you may receive other letters containing news about our study of the United States and Canada. In the meantime, I hope that you and your child will enjoy working together to learn more about the physical geography of the United States and Canada.

Sincerely,

CHAPTER 1
THE UNITED STATES AND CANADA
Physical Geography

Land and Water

Lesson Objectives

Upon completion of this lesson, students will be able to:
- identify key physical features of the United States and Canada,
- explain how the physical environments of the United States and Canada affect people's ways of life.

Engage Motivate Students to Learn

Warm-Up Activity Ask students to consider the physical geography of your community. What features are most noticeable about it? Invite students to list some of these features on the chalkboard. Discuss whether these features are unique to your community or whether students would expect to find them in other places in the United States or Canada.

Activating Prior Knowledge Have students read Reach Into Your Background in the Before You Read box. Then, if possible, take the class to the top of a hill or a tall building. Alternatively, show students photographs taken from such a location. Compare how land, people, and buildings look from this viewpoint and from students' usual viewpoint.

Explore Develop Main Ideas

Prompt students to look for answers to the following questions as they read: What physical features do both Canada and the United States share? What role do the Great Lakes play in transportation between Canada and the United States? What geographic features link Canada and the United States?

Teach Solicit Student Participation

Have students write a short paragraph in which they compare and contrast the major physical features of Canada and the United States. This activity should take about 20 minutes.

Assess Assess Evidence of Learning

See the answers to the Section Review questions. Students may also demonstrate evidence of learning by completing the Guided Reading and Review and the Section Quiz from the *Teaching Resources*. If students are doing a book project, that may also demonstrate evidence of learning by showing progress on project preparation.

Name _____ Class _____ Date _____

Land and Water

A. As You Read

Directions: As you read Section 1, answer the following questions in the space provided.

1. On which continent are the United States and Canada located?

_____

2. Which country, the United States or Canada, has more land? Which has more people?

_____

3. What are the two largest mountain systems in North America? What lies between them?

_____

4. What are the names of two western mountain ranges in the United States?

_____

5. Where is the Canadian Shield located? Why do very few people live there?

_____

6. In which area does more than half of the Canadian population live? Why?

_____

7. What formed the Great Lakes? When did this take place?

_____

8. What are the two major rivers in Canada?

_____

9. Why is the St. Lawrence River so important?

_____

B. Reviewing Key Terms

Directions: Complete each sentence by writing the correct term in the blank provided.

10. The Missouri River is a _____ of the Mississippi, because it is smaller and flows into it.

11. The Great Lakes were formed by _____ during an ice age.

12. The _____ is formed by the Rocky Mountains and separates rivers flowing east and west in North America.

CHAPTER 1
THE UNITED STATES AND CANADA
Physical Geography

Land and Water

A. Key Terms and Concepts

Directions: Match the definitions in Column I with the terms in Column II. Write the correct letter in each blank.

Column I

_____ 1. a huge, slow-moving sheet of ice

_____ 2. the boundary that separates rivers flowing toward opposite sides of the continent

_____ 3. a river that flows into a larger river

_____ 4. a mountain chain in the United States that meets the Laurentian Highlands in Canada

_____ 5. the hottest place in North America

Column II

a. Continental Divide

b. Appalachian Mountains

c. Death Valley

d. tributary

e. glacier

B. Main Ideas

Directions: Write the letter of the correct answer or ending in each blank.

_____ 6. The Great Lakes were formed by
    a. the Mississippi River.
    b. the Rocky Mountains.
    c. glaciers.
    d. the Great Basin.

_____ 7. What lies between the Rockies and the Appalachians?
    a. a huge plains area
    b. the Cascade Mountains
    c. the St. Lawrence River
    d. Death Valley

_____ 8. What Canadian landform covers about half of the country?
    a. the Interior Plains
    b. the Canadian Shield
    c. the St. Lawrence Lowlands
    d. the Yukon Territory

_____ 9. Which statement best describes the Great Lakes?
    a. They are the smallest group of lakes in the world.
    b. They are the largest group of freshwater lakes in the world.
    c. They are important waterways to the Pacific Ocean.
    d. They form the boundary between the United States and the Yukon Territory.

_____ 10. The St. Lawrence River is important because it connects
    a. the Great Lakes to the Mississippi River.
    b. Canada's two major rivers.
    c. the Rocky and Appalachian mountains.
    d. the Great Lakes and the Atlantic Ocean.

Climate and Vegetation

2

Lesson Objectives

Upon completion of this lesson, students will be able to:
- describe the climates and vegetation patterns of the United States and Canada,
- explain how climates and vegetation patterns affect people's ways of life in Canada and the United States.

Engage Motivate Students to Learn

Warm-Up Activity Mention to students that some places have earned nicknames based on a typical aspect of their climate. For example, Florida is known as the "Sunshine State" because it is warm and sunny for much of the year. Challenge students to think of a climate-related nickname for your community or state.

Activating Prior Knowledge Have students read Reach Into Your Background in the Before You Read box. Encourage students who have lived in or visited other places in the United States or Canada to compare those climates to your local climate.

Explore Develop Main Ideas

Direct students to look for answers to the following questions as they read the section: What factors influence the climate in Canada and the United States? Why do lands in rain shadows receive little rainfall? What different types of vegetation zones can be found in the United States and Canada?

Teach Solicit Student Participation

Have students write weather reports about two places in the United States and Canada. They may choose any two locations but must clearly identify each. Reports should be based on information from the section and should include data about vegetation. Students may also consult the climate regions map in the Activity Atlas. Students may deliver their reports orally if they wish. This activity should take about 25 minutes.

Assess Assess Evidence of Learning

See the answers to the Section Review questions. Students may also demonstrate evidence of learning by completing the Guided Reading and Review and the Section Quiz from the *Teaching Resources*. If students are doing a book project, that may also demonstrate evidence of learning by showing progress on project preparation.

CHAPTER 1
THE UNITED STATES AND CANADA
Physical Geography

Climate and Vegetation

A. As You Read

Directions: As you read Section 2, fill in the table below with details about the climate and vegetation of the United States and Canada.

Climate and Vegetation of the United States and Canada

Climates of Canada	1.
Climates of the United States	2.
Vegetation Zone— Tundra	3.
Vegetation Zone— Grassland	4.
Vegetation Zone— Desert Scrub	5.
Vegetation Zone— Forest	6.

B. Reviewing Key Terms

Directions: For each definition below, write the correct key term in the blank provided.

  7. an area on the dry, sheltered side of a mountain that receives very little rain

  _____

  8. permanently frozen subsoil _____

  9. a region of flat or rolling land covered with tall grasses _____

  10. a political division in Canada that is similar to a state in the United States

  _____

SECTION QUIZ

Climate and Vegetation

A. Key Terms and Concepts

Directions: Read the statements below. If a statement is true, write T in the blank provided. If it is false, write F. Rewrite false statements to make them true.

_____ **1.** A rain shadow is an area on the wet, sheltered side of a mountain that receives a lot of rain.

_____ **2.** The tropics is the area between the $23\frac{1}{2}°$N and $23\frac{1}{2}°$S lines of latitude.

_____ **3.** The tundra is a cold, dry region that is covered with snow for six weeks of the year.

_____ **4.** Permafrost is permanently frozen subsoil.

_____ **5.** A province is a geographic division of Canada.

B. Main Ideas

Directions: Write the letter of the correct answer or ending in each blank.

_____ **6.** Factors that account for the variety of climates in both the United States and Canada include latitude, mountains, oceans, and the
    a. size of the region.
    b. distance from the Great Plains.
    c. depth of the rivers.
    d. distance from the Arctic.

_____ **7.** Much of the climate of Canada is
    a. very cold.
    b. moderate.
    c. cool.
    d. extremely wet.

_____ **8.** One strong influence on the growth of vegetation in both the United States and Canada is
    a. rivers.
    b. the size of the region.
    c. climate.
    d. the heights of mountains.

_____ **9.** The four major kinds of natural vegetation in the United States and Canada are tundra, grassland, desert scrub, and
    a. permafrost.
    b. forest.
    c. swamp.
    d. coastal plain.

_____ **10.** The largest prairie in the world lies in the
    a. coastal areas of the United States.
    b. Yukon Territory.
    c. plains of North America.
    d. Great Basin.

CHAPTER 1
THE UNITED STATES AND CANADA
Physical Geography

Natural Resources

Lesson Objectives

Upon completion of this lesson, students will be able to:
- identify resources of the United States and Canada,
- explain how resources affect the American and Canadian economies.

Engage Motivate Students to Learn

Warm-Up Activity Invite a volunteer to empty the contents of his or her backpack. Identify the natural resources that were used to make the displayed items.

Activating Prior Knowledge Have students read Reach Into Your Background in the Before You Read box. Help them identify the natural resources linked to typical activities.

Explore Develop Main Ideas

As students read the section, urge them to answer the following questions: What are some of the most important resources in the United States? How are mineral resources in the United States used by people and industry? Why are so few Canadians farmers? Where are most of Canada's minerals found?

Teach Solicit Student Participation

Have students create two concept webs that show the natural resources of Canada and the United States. Each web should have the country name in the center. Secondary circles can contain major resources, and tertiary circles can identify the resources' uses. This activity should take about 25 minutes.

Assess Assess Evidence of Learning

See the answers to the Section Review questions. Students may also demonstrate evidence of learning by completing the Guided Reading and Review and the Section Quiz from the *Teaching Resources*. If students are doing a book project, that may also demonstrate evidence of learning by showing progress on project preparation.

GUIDED READING AND REVIEW

Natural Resources

A. As You Read

Directions: As you read Section 3, complete the statements below.

1. The United States has vast expanses of _____ .

2. Until the twentieth century, most American farms were owned by _____ .

3. Four important uses for water in the United States are _____ , _____ , _____ , and _____ .

4. The United States is the second-largest producer of _____ , _____ , and _____ in the world.

5. In the Pacific Northwest, the South, the Appalachians, and areas around the Great Lakes, forests produce _____ , _____ , and _____ .

6. About 9 percent of Canada's land is suitable for _____ .

7. The Canadian Shield contains much of Canada's _____ .

8. The _____ have large oil and natural gas deposits.

9. Canada is a leading producer of _____ .

B. Reviewing Key Terms

Directions: For each key term below, write the definition in the blank provided.

10. alluvial

_____

11. hydroelectricity

_____

12. agribusiness

_____

CHAPTER 1
THE UNITED STATES
AND CANADA
Physical Geography

Natural Resources

A. Key Terms and Concepts

Directions: Fill in the blanks in Column I with the terms in Column II. Write the correct letter in each blank.

Column I

_____ 1. Rich soil that is deposited by rivers is described as _____ .

_____ 2. The dam that produces more hydroelectricity than any other dam in the United States is the _____ dam.

_____ 3. A company that runs a huge farm is a(n) _____ .

_____ 4. The Alaskan pipeline carries crude oil to _____ .

_____ 5. There are vast vegetable fields in California's _____ .

Column II

a. the Port of Valdez

b. alluvial

c. Imperial Valley

d. agribusiness

e. Grand Coulee

B. Main Ideas

Directions: Write the letter of the correct answer or ending in each blank.

_____ 6. Why are the St. Lawrence, Mississippi, and Missouri rivers important?
   a. They link the eastern and western United States.
   b. They are major shipping routes.
   c. They form the boundaries between the United States and Canada.
   d. They are the world's largest rivers.

_____ 7. Until the 1900s, most farms in the United States were owned by
   a. large businesses.
   b. families.
   c. towns.
   d. corporations.

_____ 8. The largest oil reserves in North America are found
   a. along the eastern coast.
   b. near the St. Lawrence River.
   c. along the northern coast of Alaska.
   d. near the Great Lakes.

_____ 9. Why is mining important to the economy of the United States?
   a. It employs many workers.
   b. It represents a large part of the country's economy.
   c. Minerals are shipped to Canada.
   d. Minerals are used in other industries.

_____ 10. The Prairie Provinces and the St. Lawrence Lowlands are Canada's major
   a. agricultural regions.
   b. forest regions.
   c. mineral regions.
   d. manufacturing regions.

CHAPTER SUMMARY

THE UNITED STATES AND CANADA
Physical Geography

Guiding Question:

- How has physical geography affected the cultures of the United States and Canada?

The United States and Canada are the northernmost countries in North America. These two countries are really one great landmass. The only physical divisions between them are the Great Lakes and the St. Lawrence River. Mountain ranges and plains regions run through both countries. The two largest mountain ranges are the Rocky Mountains in the west and the Appalachian Mountains in the east. Great areas of flat and rolling plains lie between the Rockies and the Appalachians. To the east of the Appalachians, a plains region runs along the coast. While the two countries share these physical features, the United States and Canada each have distinctive landforms.

The major bodies of water in the United States and Canada are the five Great Lakes. Four of these are located in both countries. The largest rivers in Canada are the Mackenzie in the west and the St. Lawrence in the east. The Mississippi, with its major tributaries the Missouri and the Ohio, forms the largest river system in the United States.

Because Canada lies so far north, it has a generally cold climate. In the far west, the Pacific Ocean creates a fairly mild marine west coast climate. However, the interior areas are bitterly cold in winter and quite hot in summer. The United States has a much greater variety of climates than Canada. The southernmost regions of Florida and Hawaii are in the tropics. The west coast of the United States, like that of Canada, has a mild marine climate. To the east of the western mountain ranges, a rain shadow is responsible for vast deserts and arid regions. The eastern United States has different types of continental climates, which vary according to latitude.

There are four major kinds of natural vegetation within the United States and Canada. They are tundra, which is found in the far northern regions; grassland; desert scrub; and forest. Grasslands are commonly found on the plains of both countries. Desert scrub grows in the arid regions of the United States. Forests cover nearly one third of the United States and almost one half of Canada. The United States has vast expanses of fertile soil. In contrast, only 9 percent of Canada's land is suitable for farming. Both countries have abundant water, forest, mineral, and energy resources.

THE UNITED STATES AND CANADA
Physical Geography

Directions: Read the following sentences. The words in bold type make each sentence false. Rewrite each sentence on a separate sheet of paper, replacing the word(s) in bold type to make it true. Use your textbook if you need help. Key terms from your textbook are underlined. If necessary, look up the terms in your textbook glossary.

1. When ancient <u>glaciers</u> melted, they **dug deep depressions in the land.**

2. A <u>tributary</u> is a **river or stream that flows into a smaller river.**

3. The mountain boundary that separates **animals migrating toward the opposite sides of a continent** is called the <u>Continental Divide</u>.

4. A <u>rain shadow</u> is an area on the side of a mountain **where the sun rarely shines.**

5. The area between the **$23\frac{1}{2}°$N and $23\frac{1}{2}°$S lines of longitude** is called the <u>tropics.</u>

6. The <u>tundra</u> of far northern Canada is **an excellent place for farming.**

7. During the summer, the surface of <u>permafrost</u> **remains frozen.**

8. You will find <u>prairies</u> in areas that **have dry climates.**

9. A Canadian <u>province</u> is **similar to a city in the United States.**

10. Fertile <u>alluvial</u> soil is left by **glaciers.**

11. <u>Agribusinesses</u> are **huge farms that are run by families.**

12. <u>Hydroelectricity</u> can be generated by **bridges built across rivers.**

Name _____ Class _____ Date _____

THE UNITED STATES AND CANADA
Physical Geography

Directions: Use the information in Chapter 1 of your textbook to place the labels on the map. Then create a color key and color these major vegetation zones: tundra, grassland, desert scrub, and forest.

Atlantic Ocean	Appalachian	Cascade
Pacific Ocean	Mountains	Mountains
Arctic Ocean	Laurentian	Coast Mountains
Gulf of Mexico	Highlands	Canadian Shield
St. Lawrence River	Interior Plains	Mackenzie River
Hudson Bay	Great Plains	Mississippi River
Great Lakes	Central Plains	Ohio River
Rocky Mountains	Sierra Nevada	Missouri River

THE UNITED STATES AND CANADA
Physical Geography

Banff National Park in Canada

Directions: Read the passage about Canada's most famous national park. Then choose one of the activities to complete.

Canada's oldest and best-known national park is Banff National Park in the Rocky Mountains of Alberta. The park is famous for its spectacular scenery. Many of its features were shaped by *glaciers,* which are huge masses of slowly moving ice. Banff has hundreds of glaciers. One of them, the Columbia Icefield, is the largest icecap, or ice field, in the Rockies. This glacier is about 40,000 years old.

Glaciers feed Lake Louise, one of the many beautiful lakes in Banff. Because the mountains shelter the lake, its surface is seldom ruffled by wind. The water of the quiet, peaceful lake is an electric shade of turquoise. The color results from the glacial meltwater, which is full of silt. Sunlight reflecting off the silt gives the lake its turquoise color. The unusual color impresses tourists so much that a park employee says, "People ask us what we put in the water to make it that color. They can't believe it's real."

Activities

- Find out more about Banff National Park and create a brochure describing its physical features, wildlife, vegetation, and tourist facilities.
- Investigate how glaciers once covered Canada and helped form Canada's landscape. Prepare a written or an oral report.
- Explore another of Canada's national parks. Create a poster highlighting its features.
- Report on the effects of too many tourists on both Banff National Park in Canada and Yellowstone National Park in the United States.

CHAPTER
1

THE UNITED STATES AND CANADA
Physical Geography

Recognizing Cause and Effect

How the Grand Canyon Was Carved

Directions: Read the following excerpt from an article about the Colorado River, in the Grand Canyon of Arizona. Then answer the questions. Write your answers on the back of this page.

"It's a real-life journey down the Colorado River to the bottom of Arizona's Grand Canyon—in a raft. . . .

As you ride the river downhill through Earth's rocky crust, you descend through layers of rock. The relatively young rocks, closest to the surface, hold fossils of 65-million-year-old dinosaurs. Below lie layers dating back nearly 2 *billion* years, to a time when single-cell sea critters were the only living things on Earth.

How did the Grand Canyon get this layered look? Way back before the canyon existed, Foster explains, an ancient sea covered the western part of North America. For millions of years, sand and the shells of tiny sea organisms settled to the bottom. Pressure from the water and the layers of more debris that landed above gradually compressed and hardened these *sediments*. The result: layers of *sedimentary rock*—sandstone, shale, and limestone—atop much older bedrock, made of schist and granite, beneath this ancient sea.

Less than 100 million years ago, explains Ivo Lucchitto of the U.S. Geological Survey, for reasons scientists still don't fully understand, the ancient seabed began to rise, forming a plateau on the western edge of the continent. Eventually the *plateau* reached 9,000 feet above sea level.

As a result of this *uplift,* the waters of the Colorado River, with its origins in the Rocky Mountains, cascaded steeply toward the Gulf of California. Flowing down that steep slope gave the water (and the sediments it carries) enormous energy—enough to cut a rift nearly two kilometers deep into the plateau."

From *Science World,* September 2, 1994. Copyright © 1994 by Scholastic Inc. Reprinted by permission of Scholastic Inc.

1. Explain how the sedimentary rock of the Grand Canyon was formed.

2. Describe the results of the uplift of the ancient seabed.

3. Explain how the Colorado River carved the Grand Canyon.

THE UNITED STATES AND CANADA
Shaped by History

CHAPTER
2

Social Studies Hot Line

Dear Family,

During the next few days, we will be studying the history of the United States and Canada. We will begin to learn about the peoples who first inhabited North America, then move on to how their lives were affected by the arrival of the Europeans. We will then learn how each country became independent and grew to become a major industrial power.

Your child will complete a special project to widen his or her knowledge of the United States and Canada. Possible projects include writing a children's book for younger children, creating a time line of the history of your community, setting up a weather station to measure and record local weather, and making a diorama of the United States and Canada or of a smaller region. You can help your child with these projects by adding your own stories and information about the community or by helping to collect weather information about other parts of the country.

Because there is a great deal of material in this chapter, it might be a good idea to focus on one particular period or event with your child, to help him or her understand it better. Perhaps you can find a historical novel to read together. You and your child might also visit places of historical interest in our community and discuss why they are important.

I hope that you and your child enjoy studying the history of the United States and Canada.

Sincerely,

The First Americans and the Arrival of the Europeans

Lesson Objectives

Upon completion of this lesson, students will be able to:
- identify the first Americans,
- describe the effects of European settlement on Native Americans,
- explain how the United States gained independence from Great Britain.

Engage Motivate Students to Learn

Warm-Up Activity Ask the class to answer the following questions as well as they can:
- Who were the first Americans?
- What were the 13 colonies?
- How did the United States gain its independence?

Students should verify or revise their answers as they read the section.

Activating Prior Knowledge Have students read Reach Into Your Background in the Before You Read box. Encourage students to think about times they have arrived in new places, such as a new school or a new community. Discuss the ambivalent feelings such experiences sometimes produce.

Explore Develop Main Ideas

As students read the section text, prompt them to answer these questions: Who were the first Americans and how did their lives change after 1492? Why did English and French settlers come to the Americas? Why did American colonists want to become independent? What are the Declaration of Independence and the Constitution?

Teach Solicit Student Participation

Have students create a sequence chart showing the events discussed in the section. Suggest boxes linked by arrows as a chart format. Students may note cause-and-effect relationships among events if these can be supported by the text. This activity should take about 20 minutes.

Assess Assess Evidence of Learning

See the answers to the Section Review questions. Students may also demonstrate evidence of learning by completing the Guided Reading and Review and the Section Quiz from the *Teaching Resources*. If students are doing a book project, that may also demonstrate evidence of learning by showing progress on project preparation.

The First Americans and the Arrival of the Europeans

Chapter and Section Support *(sidebar)*

A. As You Read

Directions: As you read Section 1, fill in the table below with information about the first Americans and the arrival of the Europeans.

Facts About the First Americans and the Arrival of the Europeans

First Americans	1.
Arrival of Europeans	2.
English Colonists	3.
Break With Britain	4.

B. Reviewing Key Terms

Directions: For each definition below, write the correct key term in the blank provided.

5. originating in a certain place _____

6. religious people who try to convert others to their religion _____

7. a person who works for a period of years to gain his or her freedom _____

8. a large farm in the South that usually produced one main crop _____

9. to refuse to buy certain goods or services _____

10. the war between the American colonies and Great Britain _____

SECTION QUIZ

The First Americans and the Arrival of the Europeans

A. Key Terms and Concepts

Directions: Complete the sentences in Column I with the terms in Column II. Write the correct letter in each blank.

Column I

_____ 1. The people who originated in a place are _____ .

_____ 2. People working to convert others to their religion are _____ .

_____ 3. Some English settlers came as _____ , working for years to gain their freedom.

_____ 4. American colonists decided to _____ , or refuse to buy, goods made in Great Britain.

_____ 5. A large, Southern farm is called a(n) _____ .

Column II

a. indentured servants

b. boycott

c. indigenous

d. plantation

e. missionaries

B. Main Ideas

Directions: Write the letter of the correct answer in each blank.

_____ 6. Scientists believe that the first people to live in North America were
   a. British colonists.
   b. migrants from Asia.
   c. French colonists.
   d. Dutch explorers.

_____ 7. Which statement best describes the goals of the Spanish and French in North America?
   a. The Spanish wanted only gold.
   b. The Spanish wanted to take over land, but the French did not.
   c. Both were interested in furs.
   d. Neither wanted to convert indigenous people to their religion.

_____ 8. Most English settlers came to North America to own land, to be free from debt, and
   a. to learn the Native American languages.
   b. to fight the Spanish and French.
   c. to have religious freedom.
   d. to find gold and furs.

_____ 9. The cause of the French and Indian War was
   a. the freedom of the British colonists.
   b. the conflicts between the French and the indigenous peoples.
   c. the need to tax American colonists.
   d. the clash over land between Britain and France.

_____ 10. What was the Treaty of Paris?
   a. a document that ended the Revolutionary War
   b. a document that ended the French and Indian War
   c. a document found in Paris
   d. a document that inspired American colonists to fight the British

Growth, Settlement, and Civil War in the United States

Lesson Objectives

Upon completion of this lesson, students will be able to:
- identify some effects of westward movement in the United States,
- explain the causes and effects of the United States Civil War.

Engage Motivate Students to Learn

Warm-Up Activity Ask students to think of how toddlers who have recently learned to walk sometimes charge forward uncertainly and bump into things or fall down. Relate this moment in human development to the young United States during the 1800s.

Activating Prior Knowledge Have students read Reach Into Your Background in the Before You Read box. Some students may instead want to imagine their neighborhood before human settlement by mentally removing buildings and roads and adding forests or prairies.

Explore Develop Main Ideas

Urge students to answer the following questions as they read the section: What allowed the United States to double its size? What happened to Native Americans as settlers moved westward? Why did many people from other countries move to the United States? Why did the North and South go to war?

Teach Solicit Student Participation

Have students make time lines reflecting the dates and explaining events highlighted in the section. This activity should take about 20 minutes.

Assess Assess Evidence of Learning

See the answers to the Section Review questions. Students may also demonstrate evidence of learning by completing the Guided Reading and Review and the Section Quiz from the *Teaching Resources.* If students are doing a book project, that may also demonstrate evidence of learning by showing progress on project preparation.

Growth, Settlement, and Civil War in the United States

A. As You Read

Directions: As you read Section 2, fill in the table below with information about growth and settlement in the United States. Under each main idea, write two supporting details.

Main Idea A
The United States grew both in lands and industrial development during the first half of the 1800s.
1. _____
_____
2. _____
_____

Main Idea B
The Civil War resulted from conflicts over power and slavery and tore the nation apart.
3. _____
_____
4. _____
_____

B. Reviewing Key Terms

Directions: On a separate sheet of paper, write the definitions for the following key terms.

5. Louisiana Purchase

6. Manifest Destiny

7. immigrant

8. Industrial Revolution

9. abolitionist

10. Civil War

11. Reconstruction

12. segregate

CHAPTER 2
THE UNITED STATES
AND CANADA
Shaped by History

Growth, Settlement, and Civil War in the United States

A. Key Terms and Concepts

Directions: Match the definitions in Column I with the terms in Column II. Write the correct letter in each blank.

Column I

_____ 1. a person who moves from one country to another

_____ 2. a person who wanted to end slavery

_____ 3. to separate

_____ 4. the rebuilding of the United States after the Civil War

_____ 5. the change to making goods by machine

Column II

a. abolitionist

b. Reconstruction

c. immigrant

d. Industrial Revolution

e. segregate

B. Main Ideas

Directions: Write the letter of the correct answer or ending in each blank.

_____ 6. Why was the Louisiana Purchase important to U.S. development?
  a. It led to the War of 1812.
  b. It doubled the size of the country.
  c. It provided trade with France.
  d. It increased the debt of the country.

_____ 7. As new American states formed, they gave the right to vote to
  a. all citizens.
  b. all white men 21 years or older.
  c. all men who owned property.
  d. all women and African Americans.

_____ 8. What statement best describes what Manifest Destiny meant to many Americans during the 1800s?
  a. The United States had a right to own land in Canada.
  b. Americans deserved free education.
  c. The United States should own the land between the Atlantic and the Pacific.
  d. The United States was a new home for European immigrants.

_____ 9. Why did some Southern states withdraw from the United States?
  a. to trade independently with England
  b. to abolish the Fugitive Slave Law
  c. to make slavery legal in Canada
  d. They feared President Lincoln would abolish slavery.

_____ 10. What was one important effect of the Emancipation Proclamation?
  a. Reconstruction began.
  b. Many African Americans joined the fight against the South.
  c. Segregation was established.
  d. Southern states founded the Confederate States of America.

The United States Becomes a World Power

Lesson Objectives

Upon completion of this lesson, students will be able to:
- trace the U.S. path to world power,
- identify some ways in which American society has worked toward equality among citizens.

Engage Motivate Students to Learn

Warm-Up Activity Read the Civil Rights Act and the 19th Constitutional Amendment aloud to students. (The text of the documents can be found in an encyclopedia or other reference.) Tell students that laws granting civil rights and the right to vote to women are just two of the many changes that have occurred in the United States since the Civil War. Today, we may take these rights for granted; however, they represent important milestones in American history.

Activating Prior Knowledge Have students read Reach Into Your Background in the Before You Read box. Then ask volunteers to share their experiences and knowledge of city life. Urge those students with limited urban experiences to recall films, books, or visits.

Explore Develop Main Ideas

As students read, invite them to answer the following questions: How was life different for rich, middle-class, and poor people during the late 1800s? What did the Homestead Act do? What were some causes of the U.S. involvement in World Wars I and II? Why were the United States and the Soviet Union at odds during the Cold War?

Teach Solicit Student Participation

Have students create a glossary of important terms linked to the period of American history covered in the section. Students may use the section's key terms as a starting point and should add other terms that they feel are important in creating a picture of the time period. Urge students to use their own words when writing definitions. This activity should take about 30 minutes.

Assess Assess Evidence of Learning

See the answers to the Section Review questions. Students may also demonstrate evidence of learning by completing the Guided Reading and Review and the Section Quiz from the *Teaching Resources.* If students are doing a book project, that may also demonstrate evidence of learning by showing progress on project preparation.

CHAPTER 2
THE UNITED STATES
AND CANADA
Shaped by History

The United States Becomes a World Power

3

Chapter and Section Support

A. As You Read

Directions: As you read Section 3, answer the following questions in the space provided.

1. How did the Industrial Revolution affect the poor in the United States?

   _____

2. How did the United States become an important player in world affairs?

   _____

3. What was one reason that the United States entered World War I?

   _____

4. What happened in 1929, and what was its effect?

   _____

5. Which two conflicts resulted from the Cold War?

   _____

6. What are some of the major problems that exist in the United States today?

   _____

B. Reviewing Key Terms

Directions: Complete each sentence by writing the correct term in the blank provided.

7. In the late 1800s, many immigrants came to the United States and became part of a huge

   _____ .

8. Jane Addams worked very hard to set up a _____ in Chicago for the city's poor immigrants.

9. Under the _____ of 1862, the government gave free land to anyone who would farm it and live on it for five years.

10. During World War I, the Soviet Union adopted a form of government called

    _____ .

11. The _____ lasted about 45 years and was a period of great tension among the Soviet Union, the United States, and other countries.

12. The success of the _____ in the United States inspired people other than African Americans to fight for their rights.

SECTION QUIZ

The United States Becomes a World Power

A. Key Terms and Concepts

Directions: Read the statements below. If a statement is true, write T in the blank provided. If it is false, write F. Rewrite false statements to make them true.

_____ **1.** Jane Addams set up a settlement house for poor immigrants in Chicago.

_____ **2.** Under communism, individual citizens own all industries.

_____ **3.** Martin Luther King, Jr., was an early leader of the civil rights movement to end racial injustice.

_____ **4.** After World War II, the United States and France entered the Cold War.

_____ **5.** The supply of workers in a society is called the labor force.

B. Main Ideas

Directions: Write the letter of the correct answer in each blank.

_____ **6.** Why did the United States pass the Homestead Act?
   a. to give Americans land in Canada
   b. to attract settlers to the Midwest
   c. to encourage immigrants to come to the United States
   d. to begin the public school education system

_____ **7.** The United States gained control of Puerto Rico, Guam, and the Philippines after winning
   a. World War I.
   b. World War II.
   c. the Spanish-American War.
   d. the Cold War.

_____ **8.** Historians have identified several events that made the United States a world power: the Spanish-American War, World War I, and
   a. the Great Depression.
   b. World War II.
   c. the Roaring Twenties.
   d. the civil rights movement.

_____ **9.** What was the New Deal?
   a. the treaty that ended World War II
   b. the end of the Cold War
   c. the beginning of the Great Depression
   d. government programs designed to restore the economy

_____ **10.** What was a direct result of the United States's fear that the Soviet Union would expand its power around the world?
   a. World War II
   b. the Cold War
   c. communism
   d. the Treaty of Versailles

CHAPTER 2
THE UNITED STATES
AND CANADA
Shaped by History

Growth, Settlement, and Independence in Canada

Lesson Objectives

Upon completion of this lesson, students will be able to:
- explain the reasons for French and British rivalry in Canada,
- trace Canada's path to independence,
- explain how Canada became a world power.

Engage Motivate Students to Learn

Warm-Up Activity Write the following headings on the chalkboard: *People, Languages, History, Land,* and *Laws.* Challenge students to categorize their knowledge of Canada according to the listed headings. As students study the section, invite them to add to the list. Students may also suggest revisions or corrections to the list.

Activating Prior Knowledge Have students read Reach Into Your Background in the Before You Read box. Then ask the class to list some of this year's most popular items among students at your school. Discuss how popularity can drive sales and what companies might do to ensure the popularity and sales of their products.

Explore Develop Main Ideas

Encourage students to answer these questions as they read the section: Why was the Seven Years' War fought? What was the relationship between French Canadians and British Canadians during the 1700s and 1800s? What is Canada's current relationship to Great Britain?

Teach Solicit Student Participation

Tell students to create a children's story about the history of Canada. Using data from the section text and their own art, students should develop a narrative format while staying true to the facts. This activity should take about 35 minutes.

Assess Assess Evidence of Learning

See the answers to the Section Review questions. Students may also demonstrate evidence of learning by completing the Guided Reading and Review and the Section Quiz from the *Teaching Resources.* If students are doing a book project, that may also demonstrate evidence of learning by showing progress on project preparation.

GUIDED READING AND REVIEW

Growth, Settlement, and Independence in Canada

A. As You Read

Directions: As you read Section 4, complete the statements below.

1. Early in the settlement of North America, the French and British were

   _____ .

2. The _____ gave French people in Quebec the right to speak French, practice their own religion, and follow their own customs.

3. After the American Revolution, Great Britain divided Canada into two colonies,

   _____ and _____ Canada.

4. Upper Canada is now called _____ , while Lower Canada is now called

   _____ .

5. In 1867, Canadians won the right to control their own government without a

   _____ .

6. After its "peaceful revolution," Canada saw years of _____ .

7. Canadians entered World War I because they were still _____ .

8. After World War II, Canadian factory goods found a ready market in _____ .

9. New laws passed in 1969 spelled out ways to _____ French Canadian culture and concerns.

10. Changes in the Canadian constitution meant that Canada was completely

   _____ .

B. Reviewing Key Terms

Directions: For each definition below, write the correct key term in the blank provided.

11. speaking or using two languages _____

12. a self-governing area _____

Growth, Settlement, and Independence in Canada

A. Key Terms and Concepts

Directions: Complete the sentences in Column I with the terms in Column II. Write the correct letter in each blank.

Column I

_____ 1. A self-governing area is a(n) _____ .

_____ 2. A _____ country has two official languages.

_____ 3. In 1837, _____ , a French Canadian, organized a revolt in Lower Canada.

_____ 4. The rebel _____ led the people against British rule in Upper Canada.

_____ 5. The British king sent the _____ to find out how to prevent rebellion in Canada.

Column II

a. bilingual

b. Louis Papineau

c. dominion

d. Earl of Durham

e. William Mackenzie

B. Main Ideas

Directions: Write the letter of the correct answer or ending in each blank.

_____ 6. France and Great Britain fought the Seven Years' War because both countries wanted
   a. to control the Ohio River Valley.
   b. to control Quebec.
   c. to control the Pacific Northwest.
   d. new trade routes.

_____ 7. What happened as a result of the Treaty of Paris?
   a. The British passed the Quebec Act.
   b. Great Britain gained complete control over Canada.
   c. All French settlers left Canada.
   d. France gained control over most of Canada.

_____ 8. What did the British North American Act accomplish?
   a. Canada was divided into Upper and Lower Canada.
   b. Canada became an independent nation.
   c. Canada was no longer subject to British rule.
   d. Canada became self-governing.

_____ 9. What happened to Canada as a result of the Allied victory in World War I?
   a. Its economy suffered.
   b. Its government collapsed.
   c. It became a world power.
   d. It became independent.

_____ 10. How did the 1982 constitution change life in Canada?
   a. It made both English and French the official languages.
   b. It made Quebec independent.
   c. It made Canada independent.
   d. It made English the official language.

The United States and Canada Today: Partners and Friends

Lesson Objectives

Upon completion of this lesson, students will be able to:
- identify some environmental concerns that Canada and the United States share,
- explain how the economies of Canada and the United States are linked to each other and the world.

Engage Motivate Students to Learn

Warm-Up Activity Divide the class in half by establishing an imaginary border in the middle of the classroom. Only one half of the classroom should have access to the door, so students can retrieve water from a drinking fountain or restroom. Give one half of the class an empty pitcher, a bag of sugar, and a spoon. Give the other half of the class some lemons, sliced in half, and a juicer. Ask students on each side of the classroom to cooperate and "negotiate" to make a pitcher of lemonade. Point out that neighboring countries such as Canada and the United States cooperate with each other by sharing and exchanging resources.

Activating Prior Knowledge Have students read Reach Into Your Background in the Before You Read box. Ask students for suggestons about how to protect your community's environment. Record their ideas on the chalkboard.

Explore Develop Main Ideas

As students read the section, prompt them to answer these questions: What environmental issues must Canada and the United States address? How do the governments of the United States and Canada respond to environmental concerns? How do the two nations help each other? How are the economies of the United States and Canada linked?

Teach Solicit Student Participation

Have students create a two-column problem-solution chart headed *Problems Facing the United States and Canada* and *Actions Taken to Solve Problems*. Tell students to complete the chart with data from the text. Students may add alternate points of view about how these problems should be addressed if their ideas can be supported by facts from the section. This activity should take about 25 minutes.

Assess Assess Evidence of Learning

See the answers to the Section Review questions. Students may also demonstrate evidence of learning by completing the Guided Reading and Review and the Section Quiz from the *Teaching Resources*. If students are doing a book project, that may also demonstrate evidence of learning by showing progress on project preparation.

CHAPTER 2
THE UNITED STATES
AND CANADA
Shaped by History

The United States and Canada Today: Partners and Friends

A. As You Read

Directions: As you read Section 5, fill in the table below with details about the United States and Canada.

The United States and Canada

Environmental Concerns	1. 2. 3.
Economic Ties	4. 5.

B. Reviewing Key Terms

Directions: On a separate sheet of paper, write the definitions for the following key terms.

6. fossil fuel

7. acid rain

8. clear-cutting

9. interdependent

10. tariff

11. free trade

12. NAFTA

SECTION QUIZ

The United States and Canada Today: Partners and Friends

A. Key Terms and Concepts

Directions: Fill in the blanks in Column I with the terms in Column II. Write the correct letter in each blank.

Column I

_____ 1. gasoline or coal

_____ 2. cutting down all the trees in an area

_____ 3. characteristic of countries that have to do business with one another to be successful

_____ 4. a special fee on imported goods

_____ 5. a trade agreement

Column II

a. interdependent

b. tariff

c. fossil fuel

d. NAFTA

e. clear-cutting

B. Main Ideas

Directions: Write the letter of the correct answer or ending in each blank.

_____ 6. What happened as a result of the 1969 Cuyahoga River fire?
    a. The United States and Great Britain passed environmental laws.
    b. Pollution increased.
    c. The United States and Canada cooperated in cleaning up Lake Erie.
    d. Water pollution increased.

_____ 7. How does acid rain affect the environment?
    a. It kills plants and trees.
    b. It lowers the temperature.
    c. It increases the amount of rain.
    d. It makes air healthier to breathe.

_____ 8. Why is acid rain caused by U.S. power plants a problem in Canada?
    a. U.S. power plants provide power to both countries.
    b. Fish are brought into Canada from the United States.
    c. Canadians drink bottled water from the United States.
    d. Winds carry the polluted air from the United States to Canada.

_____ 9. The locks, canals, and dams of the St. Lawrence Seaway enable ships to move
    a. at the same water level.
    b. down the Mississippi River.
    c. to the Pacific Ocean.
    d. from one water level to another.

_____ 10. What happened as a result of the agreement between the United States and Canada to eliminate tariffs?
    a. Economic growth slowed.
    b. Free trade was eliminated.
    c. Trade between the countries has increased.
    d. Trade between the United States and Mexico has increased.

Name _____ Class _____ Date _____

THE UNITED STATES AND CANADA
Shaped by History

Guiding Questions:

- How have historical events affected the cultures of the United States and Canada?
- How do the governments of the United States and Canada differ? How are they alike?

Scientists think that the first people to inhabit North America migrated from Asia some 30,000 years ago. Native Americans eventually populated almost every spot on the continent. After the arrival of Europeans, ways of life for Native Americans began to change. Europeans forced them to move from their lands and to work in mines or on farms. Thousands died from harsh conditions and European diseases.

Along the Atlantic Coast, English settlers established 13 colonies. In time, they objected to British rule. This conflict led to the Revolutionary War, which resulted in the United States becoming independent from Great Britain. During the first half of the 1800s, the United States gained new territory. There was tremendous industrial growth in northeastern cities. In addition, Southern farmers prospered. However, the issue of slavery divided the North and the South. This led to the Civil War. The war lasted four years and tore the country apart. After the war ended, the country went through a period of Reconstruction.

During the last half of the 1800s, millions of immigrants arrived. In addition, the United States expanded its borders. Participation in the two World Wars helped make the United States a world power. The period following World War II was one of great tension between the United States and the Soviet Union. It was called the Cold War. At home, the civil rights movement challenged the segregation of African Americans and whites. Eventually, the laws were changed to give all Americans equal rights.

In the early settlement of Canada, the French and British were rivals. The French wished to set up a separate nation in Quebec. This never happened, and tension between French and British Canadians continues. Until 1837, Canada was ruled by Britain. After two unsuccessful attempts at rebellion, the Canadians won the right to rule themselves. During World War I and World War II, Canada built up its industries to become one of the leading industrial nations in the world. In 1982, a new constitution made Canada completely independent of Britain.

Today, the United States and Canada are tied together by economics. They are each other's largest trading partner. The North American Free Trade Agreement (NAFTA) strengthened trade ties between the two countries. It also established free trade among the United States, Canada, and Mexico. In addition, the United States and Canada have worked together to solve mutual environmental problems. Together they built the St. Lawrence Seaway.

VOCABULARY ACTIVITY

CHAPTER
2

THE UNITED STATES AND CANADA
Shaped by History

Directions: Match the definitions in Column I with the key terms in Column II. Write the correct letter in each blank. If necessary, look up the terms in your textbook glossary.

Column I

_____ 1. having two official languages

_____ 2. law giving land on the Midwestern plains to adults willing to farm it for five years

_____ 3. originating in a certain place

_____ 4. a refusal to buy goods or services

_____ 5. type of logging in which all the trees in an area are cut down

_____ 6. a person who opposes slavery

_____ 7. unrestricted trade between nations

_____ 8. the fight for equal rights for all minorities

9. a fee charged on imports

_____ 10. a person who has to work for a period of years to gain freedom

_____ 11. period of tension between the United States and the Soviet Union

_____ 12. the change from making goods by hand to making them by machine

_____ 13. the plan after the Civil War for trying to rebuild the nation

_____ 14. a community center for poor immigrants

_____ 15. the belief that the United States should own all the land between the Atlantic and Pacific oceans

Column II

a. abolitionist

b. acid rain

c. bilingual

d. boycott

e. civil rights movement

f. clear-cutting

g. Cold War

h. dominion

i. free trade

j. Homestead Act

k. indentured servant

l. indigenous

m. Industrial Revolution

n. Louisiana Purchase

o. Manifest Destiny

p. missionary

q. Reconstruction

r. settlement house

s. tariff

THE UNITED STATES AND CANADA
Shaped by History

Directions: Use the information in Chapter 2 of your textbook to write an important fact about each topic.

1. The First Americans

_____

2. Effects of the Arrival of Europeans on Native Americans

_____

3. The Revolutionary War

_____

4. Effects of Westward Movement in the United States

_____

5. Effects of the Industrial Revolution

_____

6. Causes of the United States Civil War

_____

7. Events After the Civil War

_____

8. The United States's Path to Becoming a World Power

_____

9. The Civil Rights Movement in the United States

_____

10. The Rivalry Between the French and British in Canada

_____

11. Canada's Path to Independence

_____

12. Environmental Concerns of the United States and Canada

_____

13. Economic Ties Between the United States and Canada

_____

Name _____ Class _____ Date _____

THE UNITED STATES AND CANADA
Shaped by History

The Importance of the Beaver to the Fur Trade

Directions: Read the passage and answer the questions.

Between the 1500s and the 1800s, the fur trade was one of the most important industries in Canada. It played a major role in the European settlement of Canada. Fur traders and trappers explored the wilderness and built trading posts, around which settlements grew.

Of all the furs that the Native Americans and the Europeans traded, the most valuable was beaver. Why did both Native Americans and Europeans prize beaver? Native Americans made robes from beaver pelts. They valued beaver fur for its warmth, softness, and strength. They considered it the warmest of all furs, an important characteristic in the frigid winters of Canada. Beaver fur was also durable. Its strong skin could not be torn, and only a very sharp blade would cut it. Among many groups of Native Americans, beaver pelts served as the standard of value in trading. In the fur trade, 1 beaver skin was worth 1 kettle, and 12 could be traded for a rifle.

Fashionable men in Europe wore hats made from beaver fur. The height of the hat reflected the wealth and social status of the wearer. This fashion in men's hats created great demand for beaver fur in Europe. And since beavers had become scarce in Western Europe, the fur had to be imported.

The trade in beaver fur flourished until the mid-1800s, when silk began to replace fur in hats. By then, few beavers were left in North America. However, laws were passed to protect beavers, and they have since increased in number.

1. Why were beavers important to the early Native Americans?

_____

2. Why did Europeans value beaver fur?

_____

3. Why did the trade in beaver fur decline?

_____

_____

4. What were some of the effects of the fur trade?

_____

THE UNITED STATES AND CANADA
Shaped by History

CHAPTER
2

Drawing Conclusions

European Views of America

Directions: The following passage is an exerpt from an article telling how some Europeans described the United States. Read the passage. Then, on another sheet of papcr, respond to the questions.

"Imagine a country where game is so plentiful that a single musket shot kills 34 birds. Streams in this land are so overstocked that hunters pluck fish right out of the water with their bare hands. And the air there is so pure that it cures illnesses and prolongs life.

Such a country may seem too good to believe. Yet this is how some of our earliest visitors described North America in the 1600s. Throughout the past 200 years, visitors to the United States have described our country and people in many ways. Some of these accounts, as above, have been exaggerated. But as you'll see, many of the beliefs that we hold about ourselves began with the insightful comments of visitors—most of them Europeans. . . .

Cheap land helped bring settlers to the [United States]. Later, Alexis de Tocqueville, a young French nobleman, noted that Americans had a desire to develop the land that seemed to be a national mission. . . . In 1831, he noted: 'Millions of men are marching at once toward the same horizon. Their language, their religion, their manners differ; their object is the same. Fortune has been promised to them somewhere in the West, and to the West they go to find it.'. . .

By the 1800s, many foreign observers were calling American workers the best the world had known. Others, however, begged Americans to relax. 'In every circle, I have met [Americans] who had suffered from nervous collapse due to stress of business, or killed themselves by over-work. . . . We have had somewhat too much of the gospel of work. It is time to preach the gospel of relaxation,' wrote Herbert Spencer, an English philosopher, during his 1882 visit. . . .

1. What conclusion can you draw about the American landscape in the 1600s from the first paragraph?

2. According to the people quoted in this passage, what characteristics did many Americans of the 1800s share?

3. How did the views of European visitors change between the 1600s and the 1800s?

From *Scholastic Update,* October 2, 1987. Copyright © 1987 by Scholastic Inc. Reprinted by permission of Scholastic Inc.

LETTER HOME

CHAPTER
3

Cultures of the United States and Canada

Social Studies Hot Line

Dear Family,

Now that we have looked at the history of the United States and Canada, we will begin a deeper study of the cultures of these two nations. Our class will learn how Native Americans, Europeans, and more recent immigrants from around the world all made unique contributions and influenced the culture in their own ways.

Your child will probably have many questions about American and Canadian cultures. An Inuit in the Arctic, a French Canadian in Montreal, a Mexican American in Texas, and a Swedish American farmer in Minnesota would probably all have different answers to the same questions. You can help your child with these questions by offering your own ideas. Discuss the experiences of your child's ancestors. He or she may have questions such as "How did they come to the United States, and from where? Were they already here when the first Europeans arrived? If not, how did they deal with life in the new country? What cultural items did they bring with them?"

Another important aspect of both countries is how cultures have mixed over the centuries. You and your child can see the effects of many different cultures in areas such as music, graphic arts, food, sports, movies, and business. Share an exploration with your child in which you find examples of cultural mixes. Help identify the cultural sources you encounter.

As you listen to, read, or view news reports, help your child imagine how members of different ethnic groups might feel about being American or Canadian citizens. What challenges and problems might they face? How might they conquer those challenges and problems?

Thank you for your help. I hope you find this study of the United States and Canada a stimulating and worthwhile experience for both you and your child.

Sincerely,

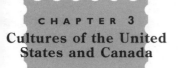

CHAPTER 3
Cultures of the United States and Canada

The United States
A Nation of Immigrants

Lesson Objectives

Upon completion of this lesson, students will be able to:
- identify some examples of cultural diversity in the United States,
- explain how cultural diversity has affected people's lives in the United States.

Engage Motivate Students to Learn

Warm-Up Activity As a class, discuss a main business street in your community. Have students list evidence of cultural diversity. For example, students might note restaurants serving ethnic foods, signs printed in languages other than English, shops selling goods and services linked to other cultures, or people wearing the clothing of their cultures.

Activating Prior Knowledge Have students read Reach Into Your Background in the Before You Read box. Then ask them how they can learn about cultural influences in their area or throughout the United States. Direct students toward sources such as the phone book, books and films available in your school or local library, or a calendar of local cultural events.

Explore Develop Main Ideas

As students read, urge them to locate answers to the following questions: How did early Native Americans learn about each other's cultures? Why do some immigrants prefer not to fully adopt American customs? What are some of the cultures that have influenced the United States?

Teach Solicit Student Participation

Have students use information from the section to create a concept web with *American Culture* at the center. Concepts in the outside circle should be influences on the diversity of American culture. Students may also include their own ideas as long as they are based on fact and related to the topics of the section. This activity should take about 15 minutes.

Assess Assess Evidence of Learning

See the answers to the Section Review questions. Students may also demonstrate evidence of learning by completing the Guided Reading and Review and the Section Quiz from the *Teaching Resources*. If students are doing a book project, that may also demonstrate evidence of learning by showing progress on project preparation.

GUIDED READING AND REVIEW

The United States
A Nation of Immigrants

A. As You Read

Directions: As you read Section 1, complete the statements below.

1. The cultures of the first Americans reflected their _____ .

2. Before Spanish explorers came to the Americas, there were no _____ .

3. Russian settlers brought with them to the Midwest a kind of hardy _____ from their home country.

4. Immigrants must decide what things from their _____ they should keep and what things they should _____ .

5. Almost all immigrants cling to things that remind them of their _____ .

6. Preserving customs helps give immigrants a sense of _____ in their new country.

7. Exchanging such things as musical styles helps us appreciate the _____ of American life.

8. Everyday items from American culture often appear in the work of _____ .

9. Cultures from around the world influence America's _____ .

B. Reviewing Key Terms

Directions: In the blanks provided, write the key terms for the following definitions.

10. a process in which ideas and customs are shared among different groups of people

    _____

11. a group of people who share a language, history, and culture _____

12. a wide variety of cultures _____

CHAPTER 3
Cultures of the United States and Canada

The United States
A Nation of Immigrants

A. Key Terms and Concepts

Directions: Match the definitions in Column I with the terms in Column II. Write the correct letter in each blank.

Column I

_____ 1. a process in which different cultures share ideas and ways of doing things

_____ 2. a group of people who share a language, history, and culture

_____ 3. a wide variety of cultures

_____ 4. a person who moves from one country to another

_____ 5. a variety of landforms, climates, and vegetation

Column II

a. ethnic group

b. immigrant

c. cultural exchange

d. geographic diversity

e. cultural diversity

B. Main Ideas

Directions: Write the letter of the correct answer or ending in each blank.

_____ 6. What is one way in which Native American groups shared their ideas?
   a. through books
   b. through trade
   c. through farming
   d. through forestry

_____ 7. Which statement best describes the cultural exchange between Native Americans and early European settlers in North America?
   a. Europeans refused to be influenced by Native American culture.
   b. Native Americans refused to be influenced by European culture.
   c. Europeans and Native Americans both changed.
   d. Europeans changed Native American life.

_____ 8. What is one way in which immigrants must change when they move to a new country?
   a. They must give up all their old customs.
   b. They must learn the language, laws, and manners of their new land.
   c. They must ignore other immigrants.
   d. They must refuse to speak the language of their new land.

_____ 9. In the United States, pastimes, foods, accents, and music
   a. are the same everywhere.
   b. vary from region to region.
   c. all originated in Russia.
   d. are the same as in Canada.

_____ 10. The United States is a culturally diverse country because
   a. it has one ethnic group.
   b. immigrants live here.
   c. it is so large.
   d. most people live in cities.

Canada: A Mosaic

Lesson Objectives

Upon completion of this lesson, students will be able to:
- identify some ways that Canada's peoples have stayed culturally distinct,
- explain how Canada's indigenous peoples have preserved their cultures.

Engage Motivate Students to Learn

Warm-Up Activity Prompt students to think about the people in their neighborhood. Ask them to describe some ways in which their neighbors are similar to or different from them. Discuss how neighbors can help one another, and brainstorm some rules for maintaining good relationships between neighbors.

Activating Prior Knowledge Have students read Reach Into Your Background in the Before You Read box. Urge them to name some of the "pieces" that make up Canada's cultural mosaic.

Explore Develop Main Ideas

Challenge students to answer the following questions as they read: What effects do Canada's two official languages have on the everyday lives of Canadians? What are some of the concerns of Canada's indigenous peoples? How have Canadians expressed different aspects of their cultures?

Teach Solicit Student Participation

Have students develop a layout for an Internet website about Canadian culture. The layout should include text and graphics. Data should include information about Canada's diverse population and the cultural contributions made by various groups. Encourage students to devise four "frequently asked questions" about Canadian culture and to include answers to those questions. This activity should take about 30 minutes.

Assess Assess Evidence of Learning

See the answers to the Section Review questions. Students may also demonstrate evidence of learning by completing the Guided Reading and Review and the Section Quiz from the *Teaching Resources*. If students are doing a book project, that may also demonstrate evidence of learning by showing progress on project preparation.

Name _____ Class _____ Date _____

CHAPTER 3
Cultures of the United
States and Canada

Canada: A Mosaic

A. As You Read

Directions: As you read Section 2, fill in the table below with details about the cultures of Canada.

The Peoples and Cultures of Canada

Media	1.
French Canadians	2.
	3.
Indigenous Peoples	4.
	5.
Arts	6.
	7.
Sports	8.
	9.

B. Reviewing Key Terms

Directions: In the blanks provided, write the definition for the following key term.

10. reserve

_____

_____

SECTION QUIZ

Canada: A Mosaic

A. Key Terms and Concepts

Directions: Complete the sentences in Column I with the terms in Column II. Write the correct letter in each blank.

Column I

_____ 1. The ____ developed new techniques in their paintings of Canada's landscape.

_____ 2. An area that the government has set aside for indigenous people to live in is called a ____ .

_____ 3. The Inuits call their new territory ____ .

_____ 4. French Canadians are concerned about preserving their ____ .

_____ 5. Canadian ____ have influenced the United States.

Column II

a. Nunavut

b. sports

c. Group of Seven

d. heritage

e. reserve

B. Main Ideas

Directions: Write the letter of the correct answer in each blank.

_____ 6. The two national languages of Canada are
   a. Chinese and French.
   b. English and French.
   c. English and Chinese.
   d. French and Spanish.

_____ 7. How do many French Canadians show their concern about preserving their heritage?
   a. They want Quebec to become a colony of France.
   b. They want French to be the official language of Canada.
   c. They want to adopt the French constitution.
   d. They want Quebec to become a separate country.

_____ 8. To preserve indigenous culture, the Canadian government passed laws
   a. allowing indigenous peoples to create a separate nation.
   b. allowing indigenous peoples to live on reserves.
   c. permitting their languages to be the official languages of the country.
   d. allowing indigenous peoples to use their own languages in their schools.

_____ 9. How did the Canadian government help the Inuits regain their cultural identity?
   a. It granted them land.
   b. It made them live in large cities.
   c. It taught them traditional skills.
   d. It made them buy food.

_____ 10. What is one cultural issue that unites most Canadians?
   a. the influence of French culture
   b. the influence of American culture
   c. the influence of the Inuits
   d. the influence of the Chippewas

Cultures of the United States and Canada

Guiding Questions:
- How have historical events affected the cultures of the United States and Canada?
- How has the variety of people in the United States and Canada benefited and challenged the two nations?

The area we now call the United States has always been culturally diverse. The cultures of the first Americans reflected their environments. When Europeans came, they changed the Native American ways of life. Europeans brought horses and metal tools. Native Americans introduced many things to Europeans as well, such as methods of trapping and forest survival. Throughout the history of the United States, a cultural exchange has taken place among the many different groups who have lived here.

Most immigrants from other countries hold on to some of their old customs. In this way, they can keep a sense of identity in their new land. At the same time, they have helped to enrich American culture. Artists, writers, and musicians all add to this mix by combining aspects of American culture with elements from other cultures around the world.

Canada, too, is a very diverse country. Its diversity can be seen at one radio station in the city of Toronto, which broadcasts in 30 languages. One of the largest ethnic groups is the French Canadians of Quebec. Many French Canadians want to break away from Canada to form their own country. They have struggled to have the Canadian government recognize and respect their heritage and language. Their work has resulted in Canada's being a bilingual country, in which both English and French are official languages.

The indigenous peoples of Canada also want to preserve their cultures. In addition, they are trying to address problems from the past. European settlers took the indigenous peoples' lands and forced them to live on reserves. Now, the indigenous peoples want their lands back or to be paid for lands that were taken. The Inuits have been able to convince the government to grant them a huge section of land in what was the Northwest Territories. They call their new territory *Nunavut,* or "Our Land."

Many Canadians are concerned that the United States has too much influence on their culture. As a result, they have made efforts to encourage Canadian culture. The National Film Board supports movies with Canadian national themes. Canada has many artists, writers, and musicians who focus on things unique to Canadian culture. Inuit printmakers and sculptors, for example, create images that use traditional ideas.

VOCABULARY ACTIVITY

CHAPTER
3

Cultures of the United States and Canada

Directions: Match the key terms in the box with the definitions below. Write the correct letter in each blank. Then write a sentence in the space provided that uses that term or the plural form of the term. If necessary, look up the terms in your textbook glossary, or see how they are used in Chapter 3.

a. ethnic group	**c.** reserve
b. cultural exchange	**d.** bilingual

_____ **1.** a process in which different cultures share ideas and ways of doing things

_____

_____

_____ **2.** an area of land that was set aside for indigenous peoples by the Canadian and United States governments

_____

_____

_____ **3.** having two official languages

_____

_____

_____ **4.** a group that shares a language, a history, and cultural traditions

_____

_____

Name _____ Class _____ Date _____

Cultures of the United States and Canada

Directions: Use the information in Chapter 3 of your textbook to provide the examples.

1. Two examples of cultural exchange between Native Americans and Europeans in North America

_____

_____

2. Two examples of cultural exchange between Africans and Europeans in North America

_____

3. An example of a cultural item that immigrants from a specific ethnic group brought to the United States

_____

4. Four examples from music, literature, or art from around the United States

_____

_____

5. An example of the cultural mosaic of Canada

_____

6. One way in which French Canadians are trying to preserve their heritage

_____

7. One way in which native people in Canada are trying to preserve their culture

_____

8. An example of a way in which Canadians are trying to keep the United States from dominating their culture

_____

_____

9. Five examples from art, literature, music, or sports expressing Canadian culture

_____

_____

_____

ENRICHMENT

CHAPTER 3

Cultures of the United States and Canada

Mexican American Border Culture

Directions: Read the passage. Then circle all the sentences below that state reasonable conclusions that you might draw from the information.

Along the border between the United States and Mexico is an area with a distinct blend of Mexican and American cultures. This region extends about 2,000 miles from the Pacific Ocean to the Gulf of Mexico and about 60 miles north and south of the border. The mixture of cultures in this region can be seen in many areas, including language and music.

Both English and Spanish are spoken in the border region, as well as a mixture of the two, called "Spanglish." One feature of Spanglish is that Spanish and English words are often blended in one sentence. An example is "Cómo se llama that place?" meaning "What's the name of that place?"

The music of the border region is called Tejano. It blends Mexican musical styles with American rock and roll, pop, country, rap, and jazz. The words to Tejano songs might be in English, Spanish, or Spanglish.

On either side of the border are twin cities, such as Eagle Pass/Piedras Negras and Laredo/Nuevo Laredo. With a border-crossing card, people can cross back and forth to shop or work. Many people share the feeling of Mexican American author Denise Chávez, a native of the region, who describes herself as "a person with one foot on each side of that border."

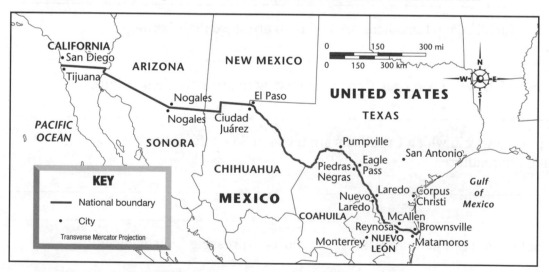

1. The economies of the twin cities along the border are interdependent.

2. The border culture extends across a large area.

3. American culture almost completely dominates the border region.

4. Mexican culture almost completely dominates the border region.

Cultures of the United States and Canada

Making Comparisons

Canadian Culture

Directions: Read this excerpt from an article written by a Polish journalist working in Canada. Then copy the comparison chart below onto another sheet of paper. Fill in the chart with characteristics of American and Canadian cultures described in the excerpt.

"The basic difference between Americans and Canadians lies in their definitions of the individual in society. The American Declaration of Independence defines the goal of society in an individualistic way: 'Life, liberty, and the pursuit of happiness.' The Canadian constitution describes national aspirations in a more collective way: 'Peace, order, and good government.' . . . I could end this article right here. Most of the remaining differences in national character and philosophy stem from this fundamental difference. But the anecdotal material is so rich that I would like readers to bear with me for a bit longer. . . .

The first anecdote: Guests are beginning to arrive at a lecture by a popular personality. The first three rows are occupied by a noisy bunch of people who shout and laugh loudly. These are the Americans. By the door stands a group speaking in whispers and waiting for the decision of the organizer to find out where it would be all right to sit. These are the Canadians.

Second: To distinguish Americans from Canadians in a group, listen for the most widely used expression. If it is 'Sure!'—they are Americans. But if it is 'Sorry!'—they are Canadians.

As in every stereotype, every generalization, there are shortcomings in these observations. There are Canadians who behave like Americans and Americans who are closer to the Canadian stereotype."

	Americans	**Canadians**
Definition of Individual in Society	I.	2.
Manners and Behavior	3.	4.

By Jerzy Jastrzebowski, Rzeczpospolita, Warsaw, in *World Press Review,* September 1994. Reprinted by permission.

LETTER HOME

Exploring the United States

Social Studies Hot Line

Dear Family,

As part of our continuing study of the United States and Canada, we are beginning to explore the regions of the United States. During the next few days, we will study four areas: the Northeast, the South, the Midwest, and the West. We will look at each region's history, growth, development, and the challenges it faces today.

You might help your child at the beginning of our study by talking about the region of the country in which we live. Ask questions such as "How is our region different from other areas? What regions are similar to ours? What historical events are important to our community and its neighboring areas?" If there is a local historical society, it might be interesting to contact them for information about the people who first settled in our region.

As your child reads about other parts of the country, you can help expand upon his or her studies by finding news articles or reports about various regional subjects. For example, you might share information about Wall Street and the stock market in New York, or government activities in Washington, D.C. You might also look for reports about new developments in farming, different industries in the South, or the use and management of natural resources in the West.

Discuss with your child the challenges of population growth in cities, and how it can lead to overcrowding and a high demand for resources. Focus on how these challenges are met in our area. Perhaps you could contact friends or relatives who have experienced some of these problems in more rural or urban areas than ours. They might be able to offer firsthand knowledge different from your own.

I hope you and your child enjoy this closer look at parts of the United States.

Sincerely,

The Northeast
Land of Big Cities

Lesson Objectives

Upon completion of this lesson, students will be able to:
- identify the ways in which the people of the Northeast contribute to the economy of the United States,
- explain why the Northeast is home to people of many different cultures.

Engage Motivate Students to Learn

Warm-Up Activity Write *New York City, Philadelphia,* and *Boston* on the chalkboard. Ask students what they think these cities have in common. Then ask students to brainstorm some characteristics or impressions they have of each of the listed cities. Record students' responses on the chalkboard. Revise or add to the list during a class discussion of the section.

Activating Prior Knowledge Have students read Reach Into Your Background in the Before You Read box. Suggest that students move all their desks to the center of the classroom. Have them suppose that each desk represents a household or a business in a city with a high population density. Guide students in identifying the advantages and disadvantages of high population density.

Explore Develop Main Ideas

As students read the section, ask them to find answers to the following questions: How would you describe the population density of the Northeast? How do Philadelphia, Boston, and New York City each contribute to the nation as a whole? Why have the cities of the Northeast been called gateways?

Teach Solicit Student Participation

Have students create a "Major Cities of the Northeast" chart. Each chart should have three columns: *City Name, Economy,* and *Other Interesting Facts.* The three rows of the chart should correspond to the three cities discussed in the section. This activity should take about 30 minutes.

Assess Assess Evidence of Learning

See the answers to the Section Review questions. Students may also demonstrate evidence of learning by completing the Guided Reading and Review and the Section Quiz from the *Teaching Resources.* If students are doing a book project, that may also demonstrate evidence of learning by showing progress on project preparation.

GUIDED READING AND REVIEW

The Northeast
Land of Big Cities

A. As You Read

Directions: As you read Section 1, answer the following questions in the space provided.

1. What are some of the ways that people travel in New York City?

    _____

2. What is the Northeast's megalopolis?

    _____

3. Where are the economic centers in the Northeast?

    _____

4. Why is Philadelphia described as an industrial powerhouse?

    _____

    _____

5. What are some things for which Boston is famous?

    _____

6. Why is New York City described as our nation's "money capital"?

    _____

    _____

7. What was the first stop for millions of immigrants to the United States between 1892 and 1943?

    _____

B. Reviewing Key Terms

Directions: In the blanks provided, write the definitions for the following key terms.

8. commute

    _____

9. megalopolis

    _____

10. population density

    _____

CHAPTER 4
Exploring the United States

The Northeast
Land of Big Cities

A. Key Terms and Concepts

Directions: Match the definitions in Column I with the terms in Column II. Write the correct letter in each blank.

Column I

_____ 1. to travel to work each day

_____ 2. a region in which cities and suburbs are so close that they form one big urban area

_____ 3. the average number of people per square mile in a region

_____ 4. the city where American colonists adopted the Declaration of Independence

_____ 5. the money capital of America

Column II

a. population density

b. Philadelphia

c. commute

d. New York City

e. megalopolis

B. Main Ideas

Directions: Write the letter of the correct answer or ending in each blank.

_____ 6. What is the most densely populated region in the United States?
   a. the South
   b. the Midwest
   c. the Northeast
   d. the West

_____ 7. The economic centers of the Northeast are the region's
   a. farms.
   b. fisheries.
   c. forests.
   d. cities.

_____ 8. What is one factor that contributes to Philadelphia's reputation as an important industrial center?
   a. its location on the Delaware River
   b. its small size
   c. its vast farmlands
   d. its famous science and technology schools

_____ 9. From about 1892–1943, the first stop for most immigrants to the United States was
   a. Washington, D.C.
   b. the cities of the Midwest.
   c. Ellis Island
   d. the cities of the South.

_____ 10. The Boston area is famous for its more than 20 colleges and
   a. parks.
   b. universities.
   c. furniture stores.
   d. doctor's offices.

The South
A Changing Landscape

Lesson Objectives

Upon completion of this lesson, students will be able to:
- describe why the South's land and water are important to the region's economy,
- explain how the growth of industry has changed the South.

Engage Motivate Students to Learn

Warm-Up Activity Write the following on the chalkboard: *cotton, oranges, peaches, petroleum, coal, fish, timber, furniture, cloth, aerospace, tourism,* and *shipping*. Ask students which of the above they associate with the South and have them explain the reasons for their associations. Then tell the class that all of the items are part of the South's diverse economy.

Activating Prior Knowledge Have students read Reach Into Your Background in the Before You Read box. Discuss with students the difficulties involved in adapting to new situations.

Explore Develop Main Ideas

As students read the section, ask them to find answers to the following questions: Why has farming always been a part of the South's economy? What are some of the South's most important natural resourses? Why does transportation play a large role in the South's economy? Why is the South nicknamed the Sun Belt?

Teach Solicit Student Participation

Have students develop a quiz containing five questions and answers about the main ideas of the section. Then have students exchange quizzes and answer the questions. This activity should take about 30 minutes.

Assess Assess Evidence of Learning

See the answers to the Section Review questions. Students may also demonstrate evidence of learning by completing the Guided Reading and Review and the Section Quiz from the *Teaching Resources.* If students are doing a book project, that may also demonstrate evidence of learning by showing progress on project preparation.

Name _____ Class _____ Date _____

CHAPTER 4
Exploring the
United States

The South
A Changing Landscape

A. As You Read

Directions: As you read Section 2, fill in the table below with information about the South. Write two details for each topic.

The Changing South

Farming	1.	2.
Industry	3.	4.
Transportation and Tourism	5.	6.
Atlanta and Washington, D.C.	7.	8.

B. Reviewing Key Terms

Directions: Complete the sentences below by writing the correct terms in the blanks provided.

9. Substances like plastics, paint, and asphalt are also called _____ .

10. The South is part of the _____ .

11. The change from an agriculture-based economy to an industry-based economy is

  called _____ .

SECTION QUIZ

The South
A Changing Landscape

A. Key Terms and Concepts

Directions: Read the statements below. If a statement is true, write T in the blank provided. If it is false, write F. Rewrite false statements to make them true.

_____ 1. Petrochemicals are substances, like plastics, paint, and asphalt, that come from petroleum.

_____ 2. Atlanta is in one of the slowest-growing regions of the United States: the Northeast.

_____ 3. Industrialization is the process of moving from an industry-based economy to an agriculture-based economy.

_____ 4. The South is part of the Sun Belt.

_____ 5. Washington, D.C., is located in Virginia.

B. Main Ideas

Directions: Write the letter of the correct answer or ending in each blank.

_____ 6. Colonists in the South were able to grow cotton because of the area's
   a. wealth.
   b. geography, climate, and rich soil.
   c. size.
   d. location near the Atlantic Ocean.

_____ 7. In Louisiana, Oklahoma, and Texas, companies drill for
   a. water.
   b. gold.
   c. plastics and paint.
   d. oil and natural gas.

_____ 8. What do textile mills produce?
   a. cloth
   b. petrochemicals
   c. minerals
   d. aeronautics

_____ 9. Two major ports in the South are
   a. Atlanta, Georgia, and Washington, D.C.
   b. Raleigh, North Carolina, and Austin, Texas.
   c. Miami, Florida, and New Orleans, Louisiana.
   d. New York City and Philadelphia.

_____ 10. Washington, D.C., is located
   a. in the Northeast.
   b. between the states of Maryland and Virginia.
   c. between the states of North Carolina and South Carolina.
   d. in Georgia.

CHAPTER 4
Exploring the United States

The Midwest
Moving From the Farm

Lesson Objectives

Upon completion of this lesson, students will be able to:
- explain how technology is changing agriculture in the Midwest,
- discuss how changes in agriculture affect the growth of cities.

Engage Motivate Students to Learn

Warm-Up Activity Invite students to share their perceptions of the Midwest: where it is, why it is so named, and what defining characteristics the region has. Explain that these perceptions may change as they read about some important changes taking place in the Midwest.

Activating Prior Knowledge Have students read Reach Into Your Background in the Before You Read box. You might suggest to students that they write a journal entry about introducing others to something new.

Explore Develop Main Ideas

As students read the section, ask them to find answers to the following questions: What has been happening to family farms in the Midwest? How did a recession help change the nature of farming in the Midwest? What are corporate farms? Do most people in the Midwest live on farms or in cities? What are some of the unique features of the large cities in the Midwest?

Teach Solicit Student Participation

Have students create Venn diagrams that compare and contrast family farms and corporate farms. Have students consider such things as ownership, size, business methods, and history. This activity should take about 20 minutes.

Assess Assess Evidence of Learning

See the answers to the Section Review questions. Students may also demonstrate evidence of learning by completing the Guided Reading and Review and the Section Quiz from the *Teaching Resources*. If students are doing a book project, that may also demonstrate evidence of learning by showing progress on project preparation.

The Midwest
Moving From the Farm

A. As You Read

Directions: As you read Section 3, fill in the table below with information about the Midwest. Under each main idea, write three supporting details.

Main Idea A
Most family farms in the Midwest have been replaced by corporate farms.

1. _____

_____

2. _____

_____

3. _____

_____

Main Idea B
The decrease in farmworkers has created a boom in the cities of the Midwest.

4. _____

_____

5. _____

_____

6. _____

_____

B. Reviewing Key Terms

Directions: In the blanks provided, write the definitions for the following key terms.

7. mixed-crop farm

_____

8. recession

_____

9. corporate farm

_____

The Midwest
Moving From the Farm

A. Key Terms and Concepts

Directions: Fill in the blanks in Column I with the terms in Column II. Write the correct letter in each blank.

Column I

_____ 1. Several kinds of crops are grown on a ____ .

_____ 2. A downturn in business activity is a ____ .

_____ 3. Small farms can be combined to form a large farm called a ____ .

_____ 4. The biggest city in the heartland is ____ .

_____ 5. A midwestern city, ____ , Missouri, was the starting point for pioneers heading west.

Column II

a. recession

b. Chicago

c. corporate farm

d. mixed-crop farm

e. St. Louis

B. Main Ideas

Directions: Write the letter of the correct answer in each blank.

_____ 6. Why is the Midwest called "the heartland" of the United States?
   a. It is the transportation center.
   b. It is the communication center.
   c. It is the agricultural center.
   d. It is the banking center.

_____ 7. Since 1980, many farmers have sold or left their farms because of
   a. an economic recession.
   b. an increase in demand.
   c. an increase in mixed-crop farms.
   d. an increase in exported goods.

_____ 8. What happened to the family farms that were sold after 1980?
   a. Small farms were sold to other farm families.
   b. Small farms were replaced with factories.
   c. Small farms were combined to form corporate farms.
   d. Small farms were replaced with large stores.

_____ 9. Why was Chicago a manufacturing center by the late 1800s?
   a. It was the capital of the United States.
   b. It was near major transportation routes.
   c. It had the largest population of any U.S. city.
   d. Many large banks were located there.

_____ 10. In which midwestern city will you find the headquarters of the American automobile industry?
   a. St. Louis
   b. Minneapolis-St. Paul
   c. Detroit
   d. Chicago

The West: Using Resources Wisely

Lesson Objectives

Upon completion of this lesson, students will be able to:
- identify the natural resources in the West,
- describe how people work to balance conservation with the use of natural resources.

Engage Motivate Students to Learn

Warm-Up Activity Challenge students to brainstorm a list of the "most important" natural resources. Encourage them to list basic resources, such as water, soil, and clean air. Record their responses on the chalkboard. When you have developed a substantial list, circle the resources that are found in the West.

Activating Prior Knowledge Have students read Reach Into Your Background in the Before You Read box. Invite volunteers to describe some of their recycling or conservation efforts. Ask them what difference they think it would make if everyone in the country made similar efforts to conserve natural resources.

Explore Develop Main Ideas

As students read the section, ask them to find answers to the following questions: What precious natural resources are found in the West? Which natural resources first drew settlers to the West? What were the effects of the Gold Rush? How have people affected the environment of the West?

Teach Solicit Student Participation

Ask students to use the section text and graphics to create a "Natural Resources of the West" chart. Each chart should list a natural resource of the West in the first column and the ways each resource is used in the second column. Students may add a third column for listing conservation issues. This activity should take about 30 minutes.

Assess Assess Evidence of Learning

See the answers to the Section Review questions. Students may also demonstrate evidence of learning by completing the Guided Reading and Review and the Section Quiz from the *Teaching Resources.* If students are doing a book project, that may also demonstrate evidence of learning by showing progress on project preparation.

CHAPTER 4
Exploring the United States

The West: Using Resources Wisely

A. As You Read

Directions: As you read Section 4, complete the statements below.

1. Theodore Roosevelt understood that the vast natural resources of the West would not

   last without _____ .

2. The incredible wealth of _____ has drawn people to the West for well over 400 years.

3. With the California Gold Rush of 1849, the _____ of the region exploded almost overnight.

4. After the Civil War, settlers found timber for new homes in the _____ .

5. To save parts of the West as natural wilderness, Congress created several

   _____ .

6. Most westerners today work and live in _____ .

7. Portland, Oregon, became a trade center for _____ ,

   _____ , _____ , _____ , and

   _____ .

8. The area around San Jose, California, is called _____ because there are so many computer companies there.

B. Reviewing Key Terms

Directions: For each definition below, write the correct key term in the blank provided.

9. one of the first miners in the California Gold Rush _____

10. a system of buses and trains used for transportation _____

The West: Using Resources Wisely

A. Key Terms and Concepts

Directions: Match the definitions in Column I with the terms in Column II. Write the correct letter in each blank.

Column I

_____ 1. the first miners of the Gold Rush

_____ 2. site of the California Gold Rush

_____ 3. a method of transportation that replaces individual cars with energy-saving buses or trains

_____ 4. trade center for lumber, furs, grain, salmon, and wool in Oregon

_____ 5. city in Silicon Valley

Column II

a. Sierra Nevada

b. Portland

c. forty-niners

d. mass transit

e. San Jose

B. Main Ideas

Directions: Write the letter of the correct answer in each blank.

_____ 6. Settlers first came to the West because of the area's
   a. natural resources.
   b. manufactured goods.
   c. sources of energy.
   d. cities.

_____ 7. What was one effect of the California Gold Rush?
   a. San Francisco became a prosperous city.
   b. Portland was founded.
   c. Yosemite National Park closed.
   d. Boston became an important commercial center.

_____ 8. Why did Congress create several national parks and forests?
   a. to decrease traffic jams in the region
   b. to reduce air pollution
   c. to save parts of the West as natural wilderness
   d. to attract large numbers of tourists

_____ 9. Many manufacturing industries were attracted to Portland because of the city's
   a. agriculture.
   b. mining.
   c. cheap electricity.
   d. fishing.

_____ 10. Some problems facing western cities as a result of rapid urban growth include water pollution, traffic jams, and
   a. fewer new houses.
   b. fewer industries.
   c. a decrease in population.
   d. air pollution.

CHAPTER
4

Exploring the United States

Guiding Questions:

- How have historical events affected the cultures of the United States and Canada?
- How did the United States and Canada become two of the wealthiest nations in the world?

The United States can be divided into four regions: the Northeast, the South, the Midwest, and the West. Each region has a unique geography, history, economy, and culture.

The Northeast is the most crowded region of the United States. Economic activities in the Northeast are centered in the region's cities. Philadelphia is important for its industry. Boston is famous for its high-tech companies and universities. New York is a center for financial institutions and major corporations as well as fashion, advertising, media, and the arts. Washington, D.C., is the nation's capital. The Northeast has been a gateway for immigrants.

People in the South today make a living in many different ways. Growing crops and raising animals are made possible by a wealth of natural resources and a warm climate. Cotton was and still is an important source of income for farmers, but it is no longer the only crop grown by many southerners. Drilling and mining and fishing and forestry are also major industries in the South. A shift from an agriculture-based economy to an industry-based economy, called industrialization, has taken place over the last 50 years. The South's major ports make it a hub for transportation, and its location as part of the Sun Belt make it a hot spot for tourists. Washington, D.C., the nation's capital, is located in the South.

Until the 1980s, much of the land of the Midwest was covered by small, family-run farms. However, during the 1980s, a recession drove many of these farmers out of business. Large corporations bought up the land and created huge corporate farms. The loss of so many farm jobs sent thousands of people to look for work in urban areas such as Chicago, Detroit, St. Louis, and Minneapolis-St. Paul. Today, these places are major centers for transportation, culture, manufacturing, banking, and publishing.

The primary attraction of the West has been its incredible wealth of natural resources. Once an area of seemingly limitless open space, the population of the West has grown tremendously. The first major influx began in 1849, when gold was discovered in California. Miners came by the thousands. Settlers came after the miners. For many years, people used whatever resources they needed. Finally, Congress created national parks and forests to protect some of the West. Today, citizen groups, industry, and governments are working to better manage the resources of the West and to use them wisely.

Name _____ Class _____ Date _____

Exploring the United States

Directions: Below is a list of key terms from Chapter 4. Write one sentence or phrase on a separate sheet of paper that describes the meaning of each term. If necessary, look in Chapter 4 to see how the terms are used.

1. **commute**—to travel regularly to and from a place

2. **megalopolis**—a number of cities and suburbs that blend into one large urban area

3. **population density**—the average number of people per square mile or square kilometer

4. **industrialization**—change from an agriculture-based economy to an industry-based economy

5. **mixed-crop farm**—a farm that grows several different kinds of crops

6. **recession**—a period of slow business and economic activity

7. **corporate farm**—a large farm run by a corporation

8. **forty-niner**—one of the first miners in the California Gold Rush of 1849

9. **mass transit**—a transit system of subways, buses, and trains used to transport large numbers of people

Exploring the United States

Directions: Use the information in Chapter 4 of your textbook to place the letter of each sentence from the box under the correct region of the United States.

---

a. Its wealth of natural resources attracted fur trappers, gold seekers and other miners, and loggers.

b. One of its cities is Washington, D.C.

c. It has a long chain of coastal cities that make up a megalopolis.

d. Congress created several national parks in the region to help preserve the wilderness.

e. It is a center for the cable industry and the aerospace business.

f. It is the most densely populated region of the United States.

g. Many of its cities started as places to process and ship farm products.

h. Its biggest city is Chicago.

i. It has a highly diverse economy with large cities, such as New York and Boston, that are centers of industry, transportation, trade, education, technology, and communication.

j. Its family farms have been largely replaced by corporate farms.

k. Engineers built dams and hydroelectric plants in the region to provide water and power to cities.

l. Its port cities have long served as important gateways for immigrants.

m. Some of its states are leading producers of salt, sulfur, lead, zinc, and bauxite.

n. It is one of the fastest growing regions in the country.

o. It is often called "the heartland" because it is the nation's agricultural center.

p. It has been a center of concern about conservation of natural resources since the time of President Theodore Roosevelt.

---

1. The Northeast   **2.** The South   **3.** The Midwest   **4.** The West

_____   _____   _____   _____

_____   _____   _____   _____

_____   _____   _____   _____

_____   _____   _____   _____

ENRICHMENT

CHAPTER
4

Exploring the United States

The Building of the Gateway Arch

Directions: Read the passage about the Gateway Arch. Then research one of the other American memorials listed below, or choose a national memorial or monument in your state. Describe the significance, construction, or other important features of the memorial or monument in a brochure, poster, or report.

In the 1800s, thousands of pioneer men and women set out from St. Louis to make their homes in the western wilderness. The Arch is a memorial to the will and determination of these men and women.

The Arch was designed by Finnish-born architect Eero Saarinen. The uniqueness of the Arch became apparent during its construction. Nothing like it had ever been built before, and engineers had to revise plans over and over. The engineering was so intricate that even a one fourth-inch error could cause million-dollar problems. Begun in 1962, the two legs of the Arch were built up from the ground section by section. A creeper crane hoisted the sections up, where they were welded in place. The job was as tricky for construction workers as it was for engineers.

As work on the Arch neared completion, the date for placing the final top section connecting the two legs was set for October 1965. An official ceremony was scheduled for the date. But during the night before the date, construction managers determined that the final piece would not fit. Excessive heat had caused the legs to expand. Workers brought firehoses and soaked the Arch with cold water throughout the night. The solution worked. The Arch shrunk back to normal size so that the keystone could fit in place. It took just 13 minutes to fit in the last piece.

Many viewers of the Arch feel awed and inspired by its graceful beauty and elegance. The Arch accomplishes what designer Saarinen called one purpose of architecture: to "fulfill man's belief in the nobility of his existence."

Other Memorials to Explore

Lincoln Memorial
Mount Rushmore National Memorial
Thomas Jefferson Memorial
Vietnam Veterans Memorial
Washington Monument

From *Arch Celebration* by Tom Ebenhoh and Steve Givens. Copyright © 1990 by Spiritgraphics.

Chapter and Section Support

Exploring the United States

Recognizing Cause and Effect

How the Automobile Changed the United States

Directions: Sometimes one cause can have many effects. Read the passage, which describes some of the ways in which the automobile has affected American culture. Complete the chart, listing all the effects described. Then think about how the automobile affects your way of life and add other effects to the list.

One of the major cultural changes in American life during the 1900s was the growth in automobile ownership. The first group of people who bought cars on a large scale were farmers. Before the automobile became popular, most Americans lived in rural areas. Farm families lived fairly isolated lives. They seldom saw people who lived more than 20 miles away.

The automobile also brought changes to people in towns and cities. They gained new freedom in deciding where to live, work, shop, and travel. Before they had cars, city dwellers walked, bicycled, or rode horse-drawn carriages or trolleys to their jobs. But with cars, people no longer had to live near their place of work. More suburbs sprang up as large numbers of people moved away from the cities.

With the automobile, people could also shop far from home. They no longer had to rely on neighborhood shops or on stores in a central downtown area. Shopping centers were built with huge parking lots for people's cars. Businesses such as service stations, drive-in restaurants, and drive-through banks also developed to meet the needs of automobile owners.

Even leisure time was affected by the automobile. In the 1920s, taking a Sunday drive became an American ritual. And families began to take long automobile trips to parks and resorts for vacations.

With the growth in car ownership came the demand for more and better roads. Soon, a new system of roads and highways crisscrossed the American landscape. The automobile affected the environment in other ways as well. The automobile became a major contributor to the smog that still hangs over large American cities.

Cause: the growth of automobile ownership in the United States

Effects:

_____

_____

_____

LETTER HOME

Exploring Canada

Social Studies Hot Line

Dear Family,

Our social studies class is nearing the end of our study of the United States and Canada. During the next few days, we will take a closer look at Canada, focusing on the following provinces or regions: Ontario and Quebec, the Canadian Plains, British Columbia, the Atlantic Provinces, and the Northern Territories.

As your child reads about Canada in Chapter 5, you might look together at an atlas and locate the provinces and territories that are discussed. Ask your child questions such as, "How are they different? What kinds of climate do you think they might have? Which is the most populous?"

Discuss with your child the French culture of the Quebec province. Your child may have heard news reports about residents of Quebec wanting to separate from the rest of Canada to form a new nation. Look for articles to share with your child about this conflict. Discuss how separation might affect the people of Canada. To help your child further understand these concepts, you might compare the events to similar events that occurred in the United States, for example, how the South left the Union during the Civil War, or how some Californians think the state should become two or three separate states.

As your child studies the Prairie Provinces, you might talk about how wheat is grown and turned into food products. Discuss its importance as a principal crop of the region and how it affects the economy.

Your child might find it interesting to learn more about how location can affect the culture and economics of a community. For example, Vancouver, British Colombia, is located on the Pacific Rim and has developed strong ties with countries throughout Asia. How is our community affected by its location?

Thank you for your help while we studied the United States and Canada. I hope you have enjoyed sharing your child's experience.

Sincerely,

Ontario and Quebec: Connecting Two Cultures

Chapter and Section Support

Lesson Objectives

Upon completion of this lesson, students will be able to:
- explain how Canada's history shaped its form of government,
- describe the structure of the Canadian federation,
- describe how French Canadians in Quebec have worked to preserve their culture.

Engage Motivate Students to Learn

Warm-Up Activity Ask students to suppose that their class speaks a different language from the rest of the school. Discuss with students how they would get along with the rest of the school. How might the class and the rest of the school communicate? What kinds of compromises might be needed? How could the rest of the school and the class learn about and benefit from each other's differences?

Activating Prior Knowledge Have students read Reach Into Your Background in the Before You Read box. Then have the class make a list on the chalkboard of all the traditions and holidays that are celebrated by their families and other families in the community. Encourage students to think of ways that we learn from different traditions.

Explore Develop Main Ideas

As students read the sections, ask them to find answers to the following questions: What are the similarities and differences between Ontario and Quebec? Why has Quebec's unique history led to a struggle among the people of Quebec?

Teach Solicit Student Participation

To ensure that students understand the reasons for the differences in the heritages of Ontario and Quebec, have students write a paragraph that answers the question: Why are the societies of Ontario and Quebec different from one another? This activity should take about 20 minutes.

Assess Assess Evidence of Learning

See the answers to the Section Review questions. Students may also demonstrate evidence of learning by completing the Guided Reading and Review and the Section Quiz from the *Teaching Resources*. If students are doing a book project, that may also demonstrate evidence of learning by showing progress on project preparation.

GUIDED READING AND REVIEW

Ontario and Quebec:
Connecting Two Cultures

A. As You Read

Directions: As you read Section 1, answer the following questions in the spaces provided.

1. What river forms the boundary between Ontario and Quebec?

_____

2. What are the primary languages spoken in Ontario and in Quebec?

_____

3. How did Toronto come to have such a diverse population?

_____

4. Why do so many people in Quebec have French ancestors?

_____

5. What is the goal of the separatists in Quebec?

_____

B. Reviewing Key Terms

Directions: Complete these sentences by writing the correct terms in the blanks provided.

6. Many residents of Quebec are _____, or people who speak French as their first language.

7. The _____ movement in Quebec worked to make French the official language of the province.

8. Although the monarch of Britain is Canada's head of state, Canada is completely self-governing, or _____.

9. The rocky, sparsely populated _____ extends from the Hudson Bay to the Great Lakes.

10. When great changes in a country are brought about peacefully, it is called a _____.

11. Canada's 13 provinces and territories are united in a _____.

12. In _____ of 1980 and 1995, the people of Quebec voted to have Quebec remain a part of Canada.

CHAPTER 5
Exploring Canada

Ontario and Quebec: Connecting Two Cultures

A. Key Terms and Concepts

Directions: Read the statements below. If a statement is true, write T in the blank provided. If it is false, write F. On a separate sheet of paper, rewrite false statements to make them true.

_____ **1.** The capital city of Canada is Toronto.

_____ **2.** The northern part of Ontario is part of the Canadian Shield.

_____ **3.** Montreal is Quebec's largest city.

_____ **4.** Jacques Cartier landed in Stadacona and claimed the region for Britain.

_____ **5.** Voters can cast ballots for or against an issue in a referendum.

B. Main Ideas

Directions: Write the letter of the correct answer or ending in each blank.

_____ **6.** The first language of the majority of the people who live in Quebec is
　　a. English.　　　　　　　　**c.** Spanish.
　　b. French.　　　　　　　　**d.** Italian.

_____ **7.** The seat of Canada's government is located in the province of
　　a. Quebec.　　　　　　　　**c.** British Columbia.
　　b. Montreal.　　　　　　　**d.** Ontario.

_____ **8.** Which of these things is true of Toronto?
　　a. It used to be called New France.　　**c.** It is Canada's largest city.
　　b. It is located in Quebec.　　　　　　**d.** It was founded in 1793 as Stadacona.

_____ **9.** What was one result of the French and Indian War?
　　a. Britain captured Quebec.　　　　　　**c.** France took control of Montreal.
　　b. All French colonists lcft　　　　　　**d.** Quebec became the capital
　　　　North America.　　　　　　　　　　　　　of Canada.

_____ **10.** One way that people of Quebec have helped to preserve their culture is by
　　a. separating from the rest of Canada.　**c.** speaking only English.
　　b. changing Canada's constitution.　　　**d.** holding festivals.

The Canadian Plains
Canada's Breadbasket

Lesson Objectives

Upon completion of this lesson, students will be able to:
- explain what attracted European immigrants to the Prairie Provinces in the mid-1800s,
- describe how the arrival of immigrants changed life for the region's indigenous peoples.

Engage Motivate Students to Learn

Warm-Up Activity Draw students' attention to the section's title. Ask them to explain what the phrase *Canada's Breadbasket* means. Have them speculate on the geography, history, and culture of the provinces based on this nickname.

Activating Prior Knowledge Have students read Reach Into Your Background in the Before You Read box. Point out that great achievements have often grown out of disappointment. For example, Thomas Edison endured many disappointments to achieve success. After hours of fruitless experiments, he once said, "I have not failed. I've just found 10,000 ways that won't work."

Explore Develop Main Ideas

As students read the section, ask them to find answers to the following questions: What challenges did immigrants face when they arrived in the Prairie Provinces? How were indigenous peoples affected by the arrival of immigrants? How do different cultural groups keep their traditions today?

Teach Solicit Student Participation

Have students write a short newspaper article titled "A Brief History of the People of the Prairie Provinces." Encourage students to answer the five journalistic questions. For example, *Who* are the people of the Prairie Provinces? *Where* did each group come from? *When* did they arrive in the area? *What* were some of their reasons for settling in this region? and *How* have the various peoples interacted at different times? This activity should take about 35 minutes.

Assess Assess Evidence of Learning

See the answers to the Section Review questions. Students may also demonstrate evidence of learning by completing the Guided Reading and Review and the Section Quiz from these *Teaching Resources.* If students are doing a book project, that may also demonstrate evidence of learning by showing progress on project preparation.

Name _____ Class _____ Date _____

CHAPTER 5
Exploring Canada

The Canadian Plains
Canada's Breadbasket

A. As You Read

Directions: As you read Section 2, fill in the table below with information about the
Canadian Plains.

The Prairie Provinces	1. 2.
Indigenous Peoples	3. 4.
Changing Ways of Life	5. 6.
Free Land to Settlers	7. 8.
Nurturing Traditions	9. 10.

B. Reviewing Key Terms

Directions: In the blanks provided, write the definitions for the following key terms.

11. descent _____

12. immunity _____

SECTION QUIZ

The Canadian Plains
Canada's Breadbasket

A. Key Terms and Concepts

Directions: Fill in the blanks in Column I with the terms in Column II. Write the correct letter in each blank.

Column I

_____ 1. People who have been exposed to a disease have a(n) ____ , or natural resistance, to it.

_____ 2. The Canadian Plains are sometimes called ____ because of the many wheat farms in the region.

_____ 3. The first immigrants to the region were of European ____.

_____ 4. The city of ____, in Alberta, celebrates ranching in an annual rodeo.

_____ 5. The place in Saskatchewan once called *Oscana* by the Cree is ____.

Column II

a. Canada's Breadbasket

b. descent

c. immunity

d. Regina

e. Calgary

B. Main Ideas

Directions: Write the letter of the correct answer or ending in each blank.

_____ 6. What is one way that European settlers changed the cultures of the indigenous peoples in the Prairie Provinces?
    a. They insisted that they wear European clothes.
    b. They brought diseases to which indigenous peoples had no resistance.
    c. They asked them to speak French.
    d. They established schools.

_____ 7. Why did the way of life of many native peoples in the Plains region of North America end in the late 1870s?
    a. Europeans brought horses to America to replace the buffalo.
    b. Indigenous peoples moved to large, industrial cities.
    c. Europeans began killing off the buffalo herds.
    d. Indigenous peoples moved from North America to Europe.

_____ 8. After the Canadian government offered free land in European newspapers,
    a. many people moved to the United States.
    b. many people left Canada.
    c. indigenous peoples gained new lands.
    d. immigration decreased.

_____ 9. Most European immigrants to the Prairie Provinces became
    a. bankers.
    b. merchants.
    c. teachers.
    d. farmers.

_____ 10. The Calgary Stampede celebrates the area's
    a. wheat harvest.
    b. fur trading heritage.
    c. dance heritage.
    d. ranching legacy.

CHAPTER 5
Exploring Canada

British Columbia
Ties to the Pacific Rim

Lesson Objectives

Upon completion of this lesson, students will be able to:
- identify the major influences on British Columbia's culture before the 1880s,
- explain why British Columbia has such a diverse population,
- describe how geography links British Columbia to the Pacific Rim.

Engage Motivate Students to Learn

Warm-Up Activity Call students' attention to the title of the section, *British Columbia: Ties to the Pacific Rim*. Explain that countries that border the Pacific Ocean are considered Pacific Rim countries. Then have students turn to the map in this section entitled *Trade Routes Across the Pacific Ocean*. Help students locate British Columbia and ask them to trace shipping routes from British Columbia to Pacific Rim countries. Mention to students that they will learn more about British Columbia's relationship to the Pacific Rim as they read the section.

Activating Prior Knowledge Have students read Reach Into Your Background in the Before You Read box. Suggest to students that they think of how they benefit from local natural resources. Discuss some issues regarding the conservation of these local resources.

Explore Develop Main Ideas

As students read the section, ask them to find answers to the following questions: What were some of the customs of the indigenous peoples of British Columbia? How did the arrival of Europeans affect the lives of indigenous peoples? What events caused dramatic changes in the population of the region? What is life like in British Columbia today?

Teach Solicit Student Participation

Have students create a time line of British Columbia's history. They should begin with the coming of people to the region about 12,000 years ago and continue to the present day, identifying the dates of significant events and briefly describing each one. This activity should take about 30 minutes.

Assess Assess Evidence of Learning

See the answers to the Section Review questions. Students may also demonstrate evidence of learning by completing the Guided Reading and Review and the Section Quiz from the *Teaching Resources*. If students are doing a book project, that may also demonstrate evidence of learning by showing progress on project preparation.

GUIDED READING AND REVIEW

British Columbia
Ties to the Pacific Rim

A. As You Read

Directions: As you read Section 3, complete the statements below.

1. Each of the first groups to come to British Columbia had a complex society and its own

_____ .

2. The first European explorers to arrive in the late 1500s came to _____ .

3. The lives of the indigenous peoples in British Columbia were not changed as much by

trade with Europeans as by the discovery of _____ .

4. Victoria's population doubled overnight when 450 _____ arrived.

5. The reason that _____ sprang up in the Cariboo region was because the
government built a highway to the region.

6. By the late 1800s, Canadian laws banned indigenous peoples' _____ ,

_____ , and _____ .

7. Today, indigenous peoples are demanding land and political _____ .

8. In 1881, Canadians began work on a _____ that would link Montreal
and Vancouver.

9. Many people who live in British Columbia today feel that their future lies with the

_____ , not with the rest of Canada.

10. Forty percent of British Columbia's trade is with countries in _____ .

B. Reviewing Key Terms

Directions: For each definition below, write the key term in the blank provided.

11. a tall, carved, wooden pole that contains symbols of a group, a clan, or a family of

indigenous peoples _____

12. a town that grows very quickly to serve the needs of miners _____

CHAPTER 5
Exploring Canada

British Columbia
Ties to the Pacific Rim

A. Key Terms and Concepts

Directions: Match the definitions in Column I with the terms in Column II. Write the correct letter in each blank.

Column I

_____ 1. a carved object that includes the symbols for a group, a clan, or a family

_____ 2. a settlement that was designed to meet the needs of the miners

_____ 3. small trading village established by the British on Vancouver Island

_____ 4. a place where miners discovered gold

_____ 5. nations bordering the Pacific Ocean

Column II

a. boomtown

b. Victoria

c. Pacific Rim

d. Cariboo Mountains

e. totem pole

B. Main Ideas

Directions: Write the letter of the correct answer or ending in each blank.

_____ 6. European explorers first came to what is now British Columbia in order to
  a. farm.
  b. trade.
  c. build schools.
  d. build settlements.

_____ 7. In 1858, what major event changed life on Vancouver Island?
  a. Indigenous peoples were exposed to measles by European settlers.
  b. The Spanish arrived on the island.
  c. The British built a fur-trading post.
  d. Someone discovered gold along Fraser River.

_____ 8. In 1888, how did the British government decide to change the lives of the native people of British Columbia?
  a. by forcing them to live on reserves
  b. by forcing them to move to France
  c. by forcing them to move to Britain
  d. by forcing them to sell their land

_____ 9. The goal in building a railroad from Montreal to Vancouver was
  a. to bring European settlers to Montreal.
  b. to unite Canada and the United States.
  c. to unite Canada.
  d. to bring indigenous peoples to a new homeland.

_____ 10. British Columbia's trade, diverse people, and physical geography link the province with
  a. Pacific Rim countries.
  b. the rest of Canada.
  c. Europe.
  d. Great Britain.

The Atlantic Provinces
United by the Seas

4

Lesson Objectives

Upon completion of this lesson, students will be able to:
- analyze the influence of natural resources on the economies of the Atlantic Provinces,
- describe changes in the economies of the Atlantic Provinces over time.

Engage Motivate Students to Learn

Warm-Up Activity Refer students to the section title, The Atlantic Provinces: United by the Seas. Ask them to study the map on the facing page to identify how each of the four Atlantic Provinces touches the Atlantic Ocean. Encourage students to predict what economic activities might be common in this region. What other similarities might these provinces have?

Activating Prior Knowledge Have students read Reach Into Your Background in the Before You Read box. Explain to students that sometimes information about human history is lost or forgotten. Ask students to think about explorers' excitement when they find a lost piece of history. Discuss ways in which that history can be kept alive for the future.

Explore Develop Main Ideas

As students read the section, ask them to find answers to the following questions: Who were the first Europeans to land on the North American coast? How did fighting between Britain and France affect the people of the region? What have been the region's most important industries and how have they changed?

Teach Solicit Student Participation

Have students write a travel brochure encouraging people to visit the Atlantic Provinces. Students should name the provinces and describe the geography of the region. Brochures can include information about interesting tourist attractions, current industries, and the history of the area. Invite students to draw colorful maps of the region as well. This activity should take about 30 minutes.

Assess Assess Evidence of Learning

See the answers to the Section Review questions. Students may also demonstrate evidence of learning by completing the Guided Reading and Review and the Section Quiz from the *Teaching Resources*. If students are doing a book project, that may also demonstrate evidence of learning by showing progress on project preparation.

Name _____ Class _____ Date _____

CHAPTER 5
Exploring Canada

The Atlantic Provinces
United by the Seas

A. As You Read

Directions: As you read Section 4, answer the following questions in the spaces provided.

I. What are the names of the Atlantic Provinces?

_____

2. How does the geography of the Atlantic Provinces affect the residents' way of life?

_____

3. Why were people of French descent exiled from Acadia?

_____

4. What is the focus of the economy in the Atlantic Provinces?

_____

5. How did shipbuilding change in the 1880s?

_____

6. How important is fishing in the Atlantic Provinces today?

_____

7. How did the ban on cod fishing in 1992 affect Newfoundland's fishing industry?

_____

8. What new industries have grown in the Atlantic Provinces?

_____

B. Reviewing Key Terms

Directions: Complete these sentences by writing the correct terms in the blanks provided.

9. Acadians of French descent were _____, or forced to leave the area.

10. A _____ industry is one that is related to navigation or commerce on the sea.

11. In New Brunswick, residents are employed in _____, or raising fish on farms.

SECTION QUIZ

The Atlantic Provinces
United by the Seas

A. Key Terms and Concepts

Directions: Read the statements below. If a statement is true, write T in the blank provided. If it is false, write F. On a separate sheet of paper, rewrite the false statements to make them true.

_____ **1.** L'Anse aux Meadows is believed to be the site of a Viking settlement.

_____ **2.** Aquaculture is the industry of raising fish.

_____ **3.** Banking is an example of a maritime industry.

_____ **4.** Acadia was the first French settlement in North America.

_____ **5.** Someone who is exiled from a place may visit it whenever he likes.

B. Main Ideas

Directions: Write the letter of the correct answer or ending in each blank.

_____ **6.** Which of the following is not one of the Atlantic Provinces?
    a. New Brunswick   **c.** Newfoundland
    b. Prince Edward Island   **d.** Quebec

_____ **7.** Which two countries fought over control of eastern Canada?
    a. the United States and Canada   **c.** France and Italy
    b. France and Britain   **d.** Germany and Britain

_____ **8.** One industry that has been very important to this region's economy is
    a. construction.   **c.** fishing.
    b. wheat farming.   **d.** steel making.

_____ **9.** What factor was responsible for a slowing of the economy in the 1880s in the region?
    a. Ships were increasingly made out of wood rather than steel.   **c.** Cod fishing was banned.
    b. Ships were increasingly made out of steel rather than wood.   **d.** Fish processing earned profits.

_____ **10.** One way that people are trying to expand industry in the region is by
    a. growing mussels.   **c.** raising corn.
    b. building skyscrapers.   **d.** processing pork.

CHAPTER 5
Exploring Canada

The Northern Territories
New Frontiers

Lesson Objectives
- identify the native peoples of Canada's Northern Territories,
- compare the forms of government of a territory and a province.

Engage Motivate Students to Learn

Warm-Up Activity Focus students' attention on the section title, The Northern Territories: New Frontiers. Ask students to explain what a frontier is. Have them look at the map on the facing page and identify reasons that this region might be called a frontier.

Activating Prior Knowledge Have students read Reach Into Your Background in the Before You Read box. Ask students what reasons they might use to convince others to join their efforts to create a student lounge. How could the student body raise money to furnish and maintain the lounge? Who would be in charge of it and how would this be decided?

Explore Develop Main Ideas

As students read the section, ask them to find answers to the following questions: How does the population of the Northern Territories differ from other parts of Canada? How did Nunavut become a separate territory? How do the governments of the territories differ from those of the provinces?

Teach Solicit Student Participation

Ask students to suppose they are visiting the Northern Territories and have them write a letter home to a friend describing the experience. Letters should include descriptions of the land and its people. Encourage students to write about the history of the area, recent developments, and aspects that make the region a unique part of Canada. This activity should take about 20 minutes.

Assess Assess Evidence of Learning

See the answers to the Section Review questions. Students may also demonstrate evidence of learning by completing the Guided Reading and Review and the Section Quiz from the *Teaching Resources*. If students are doing a book project, that may also demonstrate evidence of learning by showing progress on project preparation.

The Northern Territories
New Frontiers

A. As You Read

Directions: As you read Section 5, fill in the table with information about the
Northern Territories.

Geography	1.
	2.
Population	3.
	4.
Government	5.
	6.
Gold Rush	7.
	8.
Nunavut	9.
	10.

B. Reviewing Key Terms

Directions: In the blank provided, write the definition for the following key term.

11. aurora borealis _____

CHAPTER 5
Exploring Canada

The Northern Territories New Frontiers

A. Key Terms and Concepts

Directions: Fill in the blanks in Column I with the terms in Column II. Write the correct letter in each blank.

Column I

_____ 1. The capital of Nunavut is _____.

_____ 2. The _____ Territory was the site of the famous Klondike Gold Rush in 1896.

_____ 3. _____ means "our land" in the Inuit language of Inuktitut.

_____ 4. The Northern Territories are excellent places to see a natural light show called the _____.

_____ 5. The population of the town of _____ went from about 30,000 to about 1,300 when the gold rush quieted down.

Column II

a. Yukon

b. aurora borealis

c. Iqaluit

d. Nunavut

e. Dawson

B. Main Ideas

Directions: Write the letter of the correct answer or ending in each blank.

_____ 6. Why are the Northern Territories sparsely populated?
   a. It is illegal to live there.
   b. The area is mainly tundra.
   c. The climate is too hot.
   d. The northern lights are dangerous.

_____ 7. Almost half of the people living in the Northwest Territories are
   a. indigenous people.
   b. visitors.
   c. from the United States.
   d. Chinese immigrants.

_____ 8. What is one way in which the governments of the Northern Territories differ from the governments of Canadian provinces?
   a. The territories are not represented in Parliament.
   b. The territories have no legislative bodies.
   c. The territories have more power to tax.
   d. The federal government has more control over the territories.

_____ 9. Why was Dawson once called the "Paris of the North"?
   a. Many French settlers lived there.
   b. Only the French language was spoken.
   c. Many residents of Dawson had visited Paris.
   d. It had many theaters and dance halls to entertain gold prospectors.

_____ 10. What is one challenge faced by the residents of Nunavut today?
   a. becoming a Canadian territory
   b. finding gold
   c. keeping the economy strong
   d. outlawing cellular phones

Name _____ Class _____ Date _____

Exploring Canada

Guiding Questions:

- How have historical events affected the cultures of the United States and Canada?
- How has the variety of peoples in the United States and Canada benefited and challenged the two nations?

<u>Canada is a nation of many cultures.</u> People from all over the world have immigrated to Canada. Although each of the 13 provinces and territories has different histories and cultures, they are united in a federation.

<u>Ontario and Quebec are the two most populous provinces, yet these provinces have very different cultural heritages.</u> Ontario includes Ottawa, Canada's capital, and diversely-populated Toronto, Canada's largest city. Quebec was first settled by French colonists. French is the official language in Quebec. Even today, Francophones, or French-speaking people, are the majority in Quebec. Many think that Quebec should be a separate nation. In 1995, a vote on separating from Canada was barely defeated.

<u>The Prairie Provinces are located on the largest prairie in the world. They are called the breadbasket of Canada because they produce so much wheat.</u> Immigrants came to the Prairie Provinces when the Canadian government advertised free land. They had a very hard life, but eventually succeeded in creating a productive farming area. The new farmers, however, had a disrupting effect on the ways of life of indigenous peoples. New settlers killed many buffalo and Europeans brought diseases to which the indigenous peoples had no immunity.

<u>The province of British Columbia has an extremely diverse population.</u> The first great wave of people came when gold was discovered. Miners changed life for everyone. Indigenous peoples were moved off their lands and placed on reserves. In 1881, the Canadian Pacific Railway was begun, linking British Columbia to the rest of Canada. However, because of the province's location on the Pacific Ocean, many British Columbians feel they have stronger ties to the nations of the Pacific Rim.

<u>In the Atlantic Provinces, located along the Atlantic Ocean, the way of life is closely linked to the sea.</u> People of French descent were exiled when the British gained control of Acadia in 1763. Most people here live along the coast, and fishing has always been very important to the economy. As fishing has changed, residents have adjusted by exploring industries like fish processing and aquaculture.

<u>The Northern Territories are sparsely populated, and many of the residents are indigenous people.</u> The three territories are the Northwest Territories, Yukon, and Nunavut, which was formed after the Inuit people petitioned the Canadian government for their own territory. The land is rugged and the climate is very cold. The federal government has slightly more control over territories than it does over the provinces, even though each territory has its own legislative body.

Exploring Canada

Directions: Match the key terms in the box with the definitions below. Write the correct letter in each blank. Then write a sentence in the space provided that uses that term or the plural form of the term. If necessary, look up the terms in your textbook glossary, or see how they are used in Chapter 5.

a. boomtown	**d.** Quiet Revolution	**g.** totem pole
b. Francophone	**e.** referendum	**h.** maritime
c. immunity	**f.** separatist	**i.** aurora borealis

_____ **1.** a ballot in which voters cast votes for or against a particular issue

_____

_____ **2.** natural light show seen in the Northern Hemisphere

_____

_____ **3.** the peaceful change in the government of Quebec in 1976

_____

_____ **4.** a Canadian who believes that the province of Quebec should be separate from the rest of Canada

_____

_____ **5.** a tall, carved, wooden pole that contains symbols of a group, a clan, or a family of native peoples

_____

_____ **6.** a person who speaks French as his or her first language

_____

_____ **7.** a settlement that springs up quickly, often to serve the needs of miners

_____

_____ **8.** related to navigation or commerce on the sea

_____

_____ **9.** a natural resistance to disease

_____

Exploring Canada

Directions: Use the information in Chapter 5 of your textbook to complete each statement. Use a separate sheet of paper.

1. Canada has two official languages, which are

2. The majority of the population of Quebec is made up of descendants of

3. Many Francophones in Quebec formerly faced prejudice because

4. Some Francophone Quebec citizens are called separatists because

5. Results of the Quiet Revolution include the following:

6. The result of the vote in 1995 on Quebec separatism was

7. Some examples of French culture in Quebec include

8. Europeans and their descendants changed the cultures of indigenous peoples in the Plains region of Canada by

9. Immigrants from many countries in Europe came to the Prairie Provinces in the late 1800s and early 1900s because

10. The Canadian Plains are sometimes called "Canada's Breadbasket" because

11. Ethnic communities in the Prairie Provinces maintain their traditions by

12. In the mid-1800s, tens of thousands of people suddenly came to British Columbia because

13. The gold rush changed the lives of the indigenous peoples of British Columbia because

14. The reason for building the Canadian Pacific Railroad from Montreal to Vancouver was

15. Changes brought to British Columbia by the Canadian Pacific Railroad included

16. Links between British Columbia and the Pacific Rim countries include

17. Shipbuilding was an important industry in the Atlantic Provinces because

18. Scientists today believe that the northern lights, or aurora borealis, are caused by

19. The main reason for a low population in the Northern Territories is

20. In 1999 a constitutional act made Nunavut

Exploring Canada

The Canadian Identity

Directions: Read these quotes from Canadian writers about what it means to be a Canadian. Then write a one-paragraph summary titled "The Canadian Identity" on a separate sheet of paper.

"Home to me is this vastness, which is typically Canadian, and the huge distances you have to travel to get anywhere, and the weather, the experience of winter, which is bred into us out here and which we love even as we hate it—and which I think we would have had to invent as artists if it hadn't been given to us. . . ."

>—Sharon Butala of Saskatchewan ("At Home in a Harsh Landscape")

"We don't go around shouting from the housetops about how patriotic we are—it is not our style. But when people say that we have no style or mythology or history, all they mean is that we haven't an *American* history, an American style or [an] American mythology. We have our own. Most Canadians are far more patriotic than people take them for. They don't put their hand on their hearts and recite the oath of allegiance. . . . Our patriotism is not expressed in the same flamboyant way because we are a less flamboyant people. We are not a revolutionary people.

>—Pierre Berton of Ontario ("Oh Canada!")

"Haven't we always known that the greatness of Canadians lies in how good they are to each other, how kind they are? In a world of intolerance, we have shown ourselves to be uncommonly tolerant."

>—Joy Kogawa of British Columbia ("In Search of Unity")

"Certainly the people I know believe very strongly in this idea of Canada. It's . . . an affair of the heart. . . . The one great thing that has bound us together is trying to make Quebec feel part of the family."

>—Terry Glavin of British Columbia ("Community of Dreams")

"I think I'm correct in saying that 40 [percent] of Canadians are neither of British nor French extraction. And that's going to increase. There are going to be more MPs [members of parliament] in Ottawa who are originally Italian or Sikh or Chinese or Haitian. Maybe there's some hope, and they're gonna say, 'Enough of this about the two founding races. We're all immigrants here and we're bored with your old quarrel and let's get along.'"

>—Mordecai Richler of Quebec ("Oh Canada!")

From *Maclean's Magazine,* Maclean Hunter Publication Limited, July 1, 1994.

CRITICAL THINKING

CHAPTER
5

Exploring Canada

Identifying Central Issues

Totem Poles in British Columbia

Directions: Read the passage. Then circle all the sentences below that express main ideas in the passage.

Today in British Columbia, visitors can see many reminders of early cultures. In parks, museums, and other places throughout the province stand tall totem poles. Some of these poles were created in the 1800s by the Haida, Kwakiutl, Tlingit, and other groups of indigenous peoples who lived along the Northwest Coast. Others were carved in recent times by contemporary indigenous artists.

In the 1800s, indigenous peoples living in the villages along the Northwest Coast carved totem poles for several purposes. A *welcome pole* was set up near the village beach to welcome visitors to a feast. *House posts* supported the beams of houses. *House frontal poles* stood outside the front of a house and identified the family living there. A *memorial pole* was carved to honor a dead chief. A *mortuary pole* marked the remains of the deceased.

Whatever their purpose, totem poles were carved with images of people, animals, and mythical creatures. They displayed the symbols, histories, and achievements of individuals, families, groups, and clans.

To create a totem pole, a carver used the trunk of the western red cedar tree. Most modern totem poles are still carved from red cedar. Like the older poles, they portray symbols, legends, and traditions of indigenous peoples.

The totem poles in British Columbia vary in height. Those from the 1800s are up to 60 feet (18 m) high. Newer totem poles are even higher. The tallest one is in the village of Alert Bay and stands 180 feet (54 m).

1. Many totem poles can be seen in British Columbia today.

2. Totem poles vary in height.

3. The figures carved on totem poles portray the symbols, histories, and achievements of individuals, families, groups, and clans of indigenous peoples of the Northwest Coast.

4. Modern totem poles continue the traditions of indigenous peoples of the Northwest Coast.

5. The Haida, Kwakiutl, and Tlingit lived along the Northwest coast.

6. In the past, totem poles served several purposes: they welcomed visitors, supported the beams of houses, identified families, and commemorated chiefs and high-ranking people.

Answer Key

Chapter 1

Section 1 Guided Reading

1. North America
2. Canada; the United States
3. the Rocky Mountains and the Appalachian/Laurentian Mountains; a huge plains area—called the Interior Plains in Canada, and the Great Plains and the Central Plains in the United States
4. the Sierra Nevada and the Cascades
5. east of the Interior Plains; because the land is very rocky and rugged
6. in the St. Lawrence Lowlands; The region is Canada's manufacturing center, and the land is fertile, which is good for farming.
7. glaciers; during an ice age long ago
8. the Mackenzie and the St. Lawrence
9. because it is one of North America's most used transportation routes; It connects the Great Lakes to the Atlantic Ocean.
10. tributary
11. glaciers
12. Continental Divide

Section 1 Quiz

1. e	2. a	3. d	4. b	5. c
6. c	7. a	8. b	9. b	10. d

Section 2 Guided Reading

Answers may vary. Possible answers are given.

1. generally cold climate due to northern latitude; ocean influence in the west creates marine west coast climate; inland plains are cold in the winter and hot in the summer; rain shadow from Rockies makes the east side dry
2. vary greatly from Alaska in the north to Florida and Hawaii in the south; hot western deserts to the east of the Sierra Nevada; east has continental climates; north has cold, snowy winters and warm summers; south has long, hot summers and mild winters; coastal areas sometimes experience violent weather, such as hurricanes

3. far north; cold and dry with snow cover at least half the year; mosses, grasses, and wildflowers grow only in summer; permafrost
4. prairies covered with tall grasses on the plains of the United States and Canada; the western Great Plains have shorter grasses due to less rain; wheat grows well
5. Great Basin between the Rockies and the Sierra Nevada in the United States; areas have short grasses and shrubs
6. nearly one third of the United States and almost one half of Canada; The northern Pacific Coast, the Rockies, and the Appalachians have coniferous trees; from the Great Lakes across southeastern Canada and New England and down to the southeastern United States are mixed forests of coniferous and deciduous trees.
7. rain shadow
8. permafrost
9. prairie
10. province

Section 2 Quiz

1. F; A rain shadow is an area on the dry, sheltered side of a mountain that receives little rainfall.
2. T
3. F; The tundra is a cold, dry region that is covered with snow for more than half the year.
4. T
5. F; A province is a political division of Canada.
6. a
7. a
8. c
9. b
10. c

Section 3 Guided Reading

1. fertile soil
2. families
3. possible answers: drinking, farming, manufacturing, shipping, generating power

Answer Key

4. coal, petroleum, natural gas

5. lumber, wood pulp for paper, and hardwoods for furniture

6. farming

7. mineral wealth

8. Prairie Provinces

9. timber products

10. composed of material that is deposited by water

11. electric power generated by moving water

12. a large company that runs huge farms

Section 3 Quiz

1. b   2. e   3. d   4. a   5. c
6. b   7. b   8. c   9. d   10. a

Vocabulary Activity

Answers: Sentences will vary. Sample answers are given.

1. When ancient glaciers melted, they filled depressions to produce the Great Lakes.

2. A tributary is a river or stream that flows into a larger river.

3. The mountain boundary that separates rivers flowing toward the opposite sides of a continent is called the Continental Divide.

4. A rain shadow is an area on the side of a mountain that receives little rainfall.

5. The area between the $23\frac{1}{2}°$N and $23\frac{1}{2}°$S lines of latitude is called the tropics.

6. The tundra of far northern Canada is a poor place for farming.

7. During the summer, the surface of permafrost thaws.

8. You will find prairies in areas that have humid climates.

9. A Canadian province is similar to a state in the United States.

10. Fertile alluvial soil is left by rivers.

11. Agribusinesses are large companies that run huge farms.

12. Hydroelectricity can be generated by dams built across rivers.

Reteaching

Students' vegetation zones should match those on the map on page 18 of the textbook. Labels should be accurately placed on the map.

Critical Thinking

1. Long ago, a sea covered the area where the Grand Canyon is now. Sand and the shells of sea creatures settled to the bottom of the sea. The pressure of the water and additional layers of debris that fell on top caused the sand and shells to compress and harden, forming sedimentary rock.

2. As the ancient seabed rose, it formed a plateau.

3. The uplift created a steep slope, down which the Colorado River flowed. The steepness of the slope gave the waters of the Colorado River enough energy to cut the Grand Canyon.

Chapter 2

Section 1 Guided Reading and Review

Answers may vary. Possible answers are given.

1. Around 30,000 years ago, groups of people migrated from Asia; they spread throughout North and South America; indigenous groups had many different cultures.

Answer Key

2. After 1492, life changed for some indigenous peoples; Spanish settlers and missionaries treated indigenous peoples badly; French traders often lived among indigenous peoples and did not take their lands.

3. English settlers established 13 colonies along the Atlantic Coast; they used enslaved Africans to work on plantations in the South; many colonies were established by people seeking religious freedom; colonists helped Britain win the French and Indian War.

4. The British taxed the colonies; colonists objected, demanded to be represented in British government; this conflict led to the Revolutionary War, which Americans won in 1781; leaders met and wrote the Constitution, which established the framework for the government of the United States.

5. indigenous

6. missionaries

7. indentured servant

8. plantation

9. boycott

10. the Revolutionary War

Section 1 Quiz

1. c	2. e	3. a	4. b	5. d
6. b	7. b	8. c	9. d	10. a

Section 2 Guided Reading

Answers may vary. Possible answers are given.

1. With the Louisiana Purchase, the United States doubled its size; Native Americans were forced from their land; the Southwest became a territory of the United States.

2. Many people, including immigrants, went to cities in the Northeast to work in factories; the Industrial Revolution helped to create many new jobs.

3. Cotton became a more profitable crop because of the cotton gin, and required many workers; Southern plantation owners wanted to expand slavery into new western states; Northern abolitionists objected; conflict turned into war.

4. The North had more resources, while the South had experienced military officers ; the Civil War lasted four years; the North won in 1865; after the war came Reconstruction, a period during which the nation tried to rebuild; conflicts continued about how the South should be governed.

5. the purchase from France by the United States of all the land between the Mississippi River and the eastern slopes of the Rocky Mountains

6. a belief that Americans were fated to own all the land between the Atlantic and Pacific oceans

7. a person who moves from one country to another

8. the change from making goods by hand to making them with machines

9. a person who wanted to end slavery

10. the war between the Northern states and the Confederacy (1861–1865)

11. a plan for the rebuilding of the nation that was put into effect after the Civil War

12. to separate; in the South, keeping black and white people separate

Section 2 Quiz

1. c	2. a	3. e	4. b	5. d
6. b	7. b	8. c	9. d	10. b

Section 3 Guided Reading

1. most remained poor, living in crowded slums and working in factories; some settled in the Midwest

2. The United States acquired Alaska, Hawaii, Puerto Rico, the Philippines, and Guam and had a strong military and economy.

3. Germany began sinking American ships.

4. The Great Depression began. Factories closed; people lost their homes and jobs; farmers lost their farms.

5. the Korean War and the Vietnam War

6. Answers will vary, but may include homelessness, hunger, low wages, and pollution.

7. labor force

8. settlement house

Answer Key

9. Homestead Act

10. communism

11. Cold War

12. civil rights movement

Section 3 Quiz

1. T

2. F; Under communism, the state owns all industries.

3. T

4. F; After World War II, the United States and the Soviet Union entered the Cold War.

5. T

6. b   **7.** c   **8.** b   **9.** d   **10.** b

Section 4 Guided Reading

1. rivals

2. Quebec Act

3. Upper, Lower

4. Ontario, Quebec

5. war

6. growth and change

7. British subjects

8. Europe

9. respect

10. independent

11. bilingual

12. dominion

Section 4 Quiz

1. c   **2.** a   **3.** b   **4.** e   **5.** d

6. a   **7.** b   **8.** d   **9.** c   **10.** c

Section 5 Guided Reading

Answers may vary. Possible answers are given.

1. Both the United States and Canada rely on technology. But the use of certain technologies has endangered shared natural resources.

2. The United States and Canada have worked together to control water and air pollution.

3. The United States and Canada work together to maintain forests and the timber industry.

4. Economic cooperation has benefited both the United States and Canada. One example is the building of the St. Lawrence Seaway.

5. The United States and Canada are each other's largest trading partner.

6. a fuel such as coal or gasoline

7. rain that contains acid formed from the mixture of moisture and pollutants

8. a type of logging in which all the trees in an area are cut down

9. dependent upon one another

10. a fee charged on imported goods

11. trade conducted between countries without restrictions or tariffs

12. North American Free Trade Agreement, in which the United States, Canada, and Mexico agreed to have free trade.

Section 5 Quiz

1. c   **2.** e   **3.** a   **4.** b   **5.** d

6. c   **7.** a   **8.** d   **9.** d   **10.** c

Vocabulary Activity

1. c   **2.** j   **3.** l   **4.** d   **5.** f

6. a   **7.** i   **8.** e   **9.** s   **10.** k

11. g   **12.** m   **13.** q   **14.** r   **15.** o

Reteaching

Answers will vary. Sample responses are given.

1. Many groups of Native Americans with different cultures lived throughout North America.

2. The Spanish enslaved many Native Americans and forced them to work under such harsh conditions that thousands died; Spanish missionaries tried to force Native Americans to be more like Europeans.

3. The English colonists along the Atlantic Coast rebelled against British rule and fought from 1775 to 1781 to gain their independence.

4. The United States displaced Native

Answer Key

Americans; American settlers in Texas rebelled against Mexican rule; Southern plantation owners wanted to expand westward, bringing slavery with them.

5. People left farms to work in factories, cities grew, goods were made more quickly, and travel became easier and faster.

6. Arguments between Northerners and Southerners over slavery caused the Civil War.

7. Lincoln was killed; Congress took control of Reconstruction; and southern lawmakers voted to segregate blacks and whites.

8. The United States developed a strong economy and military, gained overseas territory, and was drawn into world affairs during World Wars I and II.

9. The civil rights movement began as a struggle to end segregation and gain equal rights for African Americans; it inspired Mexican Americans, women, and disabled people to fight injustice, too.

10. The French and the British fought over Canadian land because the French wanted to trap beaver for furs and the British wanted land to settle.

11. After unsuccessful rebellions, the Canadians slowly won concessions from the British that eventually led to independence.

12. The environmental concerns of the two countries include protection of wildlife, controlling water and air pollution, and forest conservation.

13. The United States and Canada cooperated to build the St. Lawrence Seaway; they are each other's biggest trading partner; and they have a free trade agreement, NAFTA.

Enrichment

1. They valued its fur for its warmth, softness, strength, and durability. They made robes from beaver pelts. The warm robes helped them survive Canada's cold winters.

2. Fur hats for men were in fashion in Europe.

3. Silk began to replace fur in fashionable hats in Europe, and beavers became scarce in North America.

4. It furthered the European settlement of Canada, and it caused a decline in the number of beavers in North America.

Critical Thinking

1. The air was clean and the land and water were full of animals and fish.

2. They were all in search of fortune in the West and were all under stress from their businesses. They worked very hard.

3. In the 1600s, early visitors suggested that life was easy in North America. In the 1800s, visitors were commenting on how hard the people in the United States worked.

Chapter 3

Section 1 Guided Reading

1. environments
2. horses
3. wheat
4. original culture, change
5. former homes
6. identity
7. diversity
8. American artists
9. art
10. cultural exchange
11. ethnic group
12. cultural diversity

Section 1 Quiz

| 1. c | 2. a | 3. e | 4. b | 5. d |
| 6. b | 7. c | 8. b | 9. b | 10. b |

Section 2 Guided Reading

Answers may vary. Possible answers are given.

1. Many radio and television stations broadcast in several languages to meet the needs of the great number of ethnic communities.

2. They want to preserve their heritage, particularly their language.

Answer Key

3. All street and advertisement signs in Quebec are in French with English translations.

4. They want to preserve their cultures and regain their lands.

5. The Chippewa sued the government for taking their land; Inuits convinced the government to grant them land in the Northwest Territory, which became a new territory.

6. Landscape painters in the 1920s and 1930s developed new techniques for painting the Canadian landscape.

7. Some famous Canadian writers and musicians are Lucy Maud Montgomery, Margaret Atwood, Alice Munro, and Gordon Lightfoot.

8. Canada has exported hockey and lacrosse to the United States.

9. Hockey teams from the United States and Canada compete for the Stanley Cup.

10. land set aside by the government for indigenous peoples

Section 2 Quiz

1. c	2. e	3. a	4. d	5. b
6. b	7. d	8. d	9. a	10. b

Vocabulary Activity

Answers will vary. Sample answers are given.

1. b; Native American groups were involved in a cultural exchange among themselves long before Europeans arrived.

2. c; When indigenous peoples were sent to reserves, they lost their traditional lands.

3. d; Canada is a bilingual country where English and French are the two official languages.

4. a; Members of many different ethnic groups have made important contributions to American culture.

Reteaching

Answers may vary. Sample responses are given.

1. Europeans brought horses to North America, which changed the way many Native

Americans lived. Native Americans taught the French how to trap and the English about local foods, such as corn and pumpkins.

2. Africans learned English and used European tools. Europeans listened to African music and ate African foods.

3. Russian farmers brought a hardy type of wheat to the Midwest.

4. Cajun zydeco music from Louisiana, bluegrass from the Southeast, Andrew Wyeth's pictures, the poetry of Langston Hughes

5. A Toronto radio station broadcasts in 30 languages.

6. by using French and promoting the French language and culture; by trying to make Quebec a separate country

7. by using their own languages in their schools and by regaining parts of their homeland

8. Canada established the National Film Board to support movies with Canadian national themes and concerns.

9. paintings by the "Group of Seven," Inuit prints and sculptures, Lucy Maud Montgomery's *Anne of Green Gables*, the folk music of Gordon Lightfoot, Canada's hockey teams and the Stanley Cup

Enrichment

Students should circle sentences 1 and 2.

Critical Thinking

1. individualistic: emphasis on individual's pursuit of life, liberty, and happiness

2. more collective: emphasis on peace, order, and effective government

3. noisy, confident, and independent

4. respectful, orderly, apologetic, and cooperative

Chapter 4

Section 1 Guided Reading

1. subways, buses, taxis, cars, and ferryboats

Answer Key

2. the chain of cities from Boston to New York to Washington, D.C.

3. in the cities

4. It is located near the mouth of the Delaware River, and important land and water transportation routes pass through it; raw materials come here from all over the world; thousands of factories produce goods that are shipped out for sale.

5. colleges and universities; science and technology centers

6. About 500,000 New Yorkers work for banks and financial institutions; the headquarters of many of the country's wealthiest corporations are here; the New York Stock Exchange is here.

7. Ellis Island in New York City

8. to travel to and from work each day

9. a region where cities and suburbs are so close together that they form one large urban area

10. the average number of people per square mile or square kilometer

Section I Quiz

1. c	2. e	3. a	4. b	5. d
6. c	7. d	8. a	9. c	10. b

Section 2 Guided Reading

Answers may vary. Possible answers are given.

1. Cotton was the most important crop for many years.

2. Today, citrus, rice, peaches, pecans, and peanuts are important crops in the South.

3. The textile industry is one of the most important industries in the South.

4. The high-technology industry and the aerospace business are two new industries in the South.

5. Miami, Florida, and New Orleans, Louisiana, are major ports.

6. The warm weather, sunny beaches, and historic cities bring many tourists to the South.

7. The 1996 Summer Olympic Games were held in Atlanta; today it is a center of trade, transportation, and communication.

8. Washington, D.C., is our nation's capital. It is home to the nation's leaders and to hundreds of foreign diplomats.

9. petrochemicals

10. Sun Belt

11. industrialization

Section 2 Quiz

1. T

2. F; Atlanta is in one of the fastest-growing regions in the United States: the South.

3. F; Industrialization is the process of moving from an agriculture-based economy to an industry-based economy.

4. T

5. F; Washington, D.C., is located between the states of Maryland and Virginia.

6. b	7. d	8. a	9. c	10. b

Section 3 Guided Reading

Answers may vary. Possible answers are given.

1. Family farms did very well until the 1980s.

2. A recession caused many farmers to go out of business.

3. Corporations bought up small farms and combined them into huge corporate farms.

4. So many people have left farms that most people in the Midwest now live in towns and cities.

5. In the mid- and late 1800s, Chicago was a center of food production and farm equipment manufacturing; now it is the largest city in the Midwest, a center of transportation and culture.

6. Detroit is the headquarters of the American automobile industry.

7. a farm that produces a variety of crops

8. a downturn in business activity

9. a large farm that is run by an agricultural company instead of by a single family

Answer Key

Section 3 Quiz
1. d **2.** a **3.** c **4.** b **5.** e
6. c **7.** a **8.** c **9.** b **10.** c

Section 4 Guided Reading
1. proper care
2. natural resources
3. population
4. Pacific Northwest
5. national parks and forests
6. cities
7. lumber, furs, grain, salmon, wool
8. "Silicon Valley"
9. forty-niner
10. mass transit

Section 4 Quiz
1. c **2.** a **3.** d **4.** b **5.** e
6. a **7.** a **8.** c **9.** c **10.** d

Vocabulary Activity
Sentences will vary. Sample answers are given.

1. Many people who work in large cities commute from the suburbs to their jobs.
2. The chain of cities between Boston and Washington, D.C., forms a megalopolis.
3. The northeastern region of the United States has the highest population density in the nation.
4. Over the past 50 years, industrialization has spread throughout the South.
5. Small family farms in the United States were usually mixed-crop farms, so that they would be protected if one crop failed.
6. The recession in the early 1980s forced many farmers to sell or lose their farms.
7. During the recession, many family farms were bought by companies, who combined them into large corporate farms.
8. The forty-niners mined gold by washing small bits of gold from streams.
9. If more people used mass transit instead of cars, we could reduce air pollution.

Reteaching
1. c, f, i, l
2. b, e, m, n
3. g, h, j, o
4. a, d, k, p

Critical Thinking
Examples will vary. Some possible examples are given.

Farm families became less isolated.

People could live, work, shop, and travel wherever they wanted.

Suburbs grew.

Shopping malls sprang up.

Businesses such as service stations and drive-through restaurants and banks developed.

During their leisure time, people took weekend drives and vacations by automobile.

A new system of roads and highways was built.

Air pollution increased over major cities.

Chapter 5

Section 1 Guided Reading
1. The Ottawa River
2. English is spoken in Ontario; French is spoken in Quebec.
3. Many European immigrants settled in Toronto after World War II, and there has been a recent wave of immigration to Toronto from Hong Kong and China.
4. Jacques Cartier claimed the region for France in the 1500s, and many French colonists remained in the area after Britain gained control of Quebec in 1763.
5. Separatists in Quebec hope that Quebec will break away from Canada and become an independent country.
6. Francophones

Answer Key

7. separatist

8. autonomous

9. Canadian Shield

10. "Quiet Revolution"

11. federation

12. referendums

Section 1 Quiz

1. F; The capital city of Canada is Ottawa.

2. T

3. T

4. F; Jacques Cartier landed in Stadacona and claimed the region for France.

5. T

6. b   7. d   8. c   9. a   10. d

Section 2 Guided Reading

1. Manitoba, Saskatchewan, and Alberta are located on the largest prairie in the world.

2. These provinces are more recent members of the Dominion of Canada.

3. The Cree, Salteaux, Blackfoot, Assiniboine, and Chipewyan were among the indigenous peoples living on the plains.

4. Indigenous peoples depended on the buffalo for their way of life.

5. People of European descent killed nearly all of the buffalo.

6. European diseases killed many indigenous peoples.

7. Many European immigrants followed the promise of free land and became Canadian farmers.

8. The Canadian government took over indigenous peoples' lands.

9. Different cultures and ethnicities are celebrated in festivals across the Prairie Provinces.

10. Wheat, the most important crop in "Canada's Breadbasket," is celebrated in events like the Weyburn Wheat festival.

11. ancestry

12. natural resistance to disease

Section 2 Quiz

1. c   2. a   3. b   4. e   5. d

6. b   7. c   8. a   9. d   10. d

Section 3 Guided Reading

1. customs

2. trade

3. gold

4. miners

5. boomtowns

6. customs, religions, languages

7. rights

8. railroad

9. Pacific Rim countries

10. Asia

11. totem pole

12. boomtown

Section 3 Quiz

1. e   2. a   3. b   4. d   5. c

6. b   7. d   8. a   9. c   10. a

Section 4 Guided Reading

1. Newfoundland, Prince Edward Island, New Brunswick, and Nova Scotia

2. The Atlantic Provinces are located along the Atlantic Ocean in Eastern Canada, and most residents live along the coast.

3. When Britain took control of Acadia in 1755, the British feared that residents of French descent might hold secret loyalties to France.

4. The economy of the Atlantic Provinces depends on maritime pursuits, such as fishing and shipbuilding.

5. Many ships began to be made of steel, which slowed the economy of provinces that had relied on forestry.

6. Thousands of residents in the Atlantic Provinces are employed in the fishing industry, and about 75 percent of all fish caught in Canada come from this region.

7. Millions of dollars were lost, and people of the province shifted their focus towards other types of fish.

Answer Key

8. Fish processing (freezing, salting, smoking, and canning fish) and aquaculture (fish farming) are two growing industries in the Atlantic Provinces.

9. exiled

10. maritime

11. aquaculture

Section 4 Quiz

1. T

2. T

3. F; Shipbuilding is an example of a maritime industry.

4. T

5. F; Someone who is exiled from a place is forced to leave it permanently.

6. d   7. b   8. c   9. b   10. a

Section 5 Guided Reading

1. The Northwest Territories, Yukon, and Nunavut make up over one third of Canada's total land area.

2. The region is mostly tundra and is very rugged.

3. Less that one percent of Canada's population lives in this region.

4. Almost half the population is made up of indigenous peoples.

5. Territories are represented in the Canadian Parliament.

6. The federal government has more control over territories than provinces.

7. During the Klondike Gold Rush, nearly 30,000 people arrived in the Yukon Territory.

8. By 1898 almost all of those people had left the region.

9. Nunavut, largely inhabited by the Inuit, was made a Canadian territory in 1999.

10. Because of its remoteness and harsh climate, maintaining a strong economy will be a challenge.

11. northern lights

Section 5 Quiz

1. c   2. a   3. d   4. b   5. e
6. b   7. a   8. d   9. d   10. c

Vocabulary Activity

Answers will vary. Sample answers are given.

1. e; A 1980 referendum in Quebec asked voters whether Quebec should become a separate nation.

2. i; Some of Canada's indigenous people believed the aurora borealis were spirits.

3. d; After the Quiet Revolution, the new government made French the official language of the province.

4. f; Separatists in Quebec formed a political party that won control of the legislature in 1976.

5. g; If you visit a traditional village of indigenous peoples in the Pacific Northwest, you will likely see a totem pole.

6. b; Francophones make up the majority of Quebec's population.

7. a; During the Canadian gold rush, boomtowns grew up quickly.

8. h; Maritime activities are the focus of life in the Atlantic Provinces.

9. c; Indigenous peoples in North America had no immunity to European diseases like measles.

Reteaching

1. English and French.

2. French colonists.

3. they spoke French.

4. they want Quebec to separate from Canada.

5. French became the official language of Quebec, to be used in education, government, and commerce; and immigrants in Quebec are required to learn French.

6. that Quebec remained part of Canada, though the vote was very close.

7. French festivals, cooking, and architecture.

Answer Key

8. bringing trade goods; introducing diseases for which indigenous peoples had no immunity, causing millions to die; killing off the buffalo herds; and taking over indigenous peoples' land and forcing them to live on reserves.

9. Canada advertised free land in European newspapers.

10. two thirds of its farmland is devoted to wheat.

11. celebrating ethnic festivals that include traditional dancing, art, and music; hosting pow-wows; and maintaining European languages and customs.

12. gold was discovered there.

13. they were pushed onto small reserves; laws banning many of their customs, religions, and languages were passed; and children were taken from their parents to be raised in European-run schools.

14. to unite Canada.

15. many immigrants came to work on the railroad, towns and cities grew up, criminals were attracted to the region, and the province became settled.

16. a coastal setting, a large Asian population, trade with Asian countries, and students' learning Asian languages.

17. much of the economy of the Atlantic Provinces was and is dependent on fishing.

18. the reaction that occurs when winds from the sun hit gases in the Earth's atmosphere.

19. the region's rugged terrain and climate, which consists of tundra with little vegetation, icy waters, and subarctic forests.

20. the third Canadian territory.

Enrichment

Students' summaries will vary, but should note the following points: Canadians see themselves as being more reserved and less flamboyant than Americans. Their identity is based partly on their relationship with the vastness and harshness of the Canadian wilderness as well as their dual French and English background.

Critical Thinking

Students should circle sentences 1, 3, 4, and 6.

Activities and Projects

Teacher Notes

To meet the needs of middle school students, **Prentice Hall World Explorer** includes activities designed for all learning styles. Every day, you encounter students who bring a wide range of skills and abilities to the classroom. You as teacher make choices about the kinds of activities that best complement your teaching plan. This booklet is designed to make it easy for you to incorporate hands-on activities into your classroom.

With support offered in this booklet, students can work independently or in cooperative groups to perform a variety of interesting and meaningful projects. For the Activity Atlas and Activity Shops, this booklet provides recording sheets, templates for graphs or charts, and helpful background information. For the Project Possibilities described in the student text, this booklet includes a section called Book Projects that offers ideas for breaking down and organizing each task.

In addition, this booklet includes cooperative learning activities for each chapter in the book. At least one of the cooperative activities is a simulation, in which students concentrate on a real-life issue. Each cooperative activity is four pages long and includes one or two student pages, one or two teacher pages, and a rubric page. The concept and skill objectives for each cooperative learning activity are clearly stated in the teacher page supporting each activity. You can customize your assignments, using particular projects to meet the needs of specific groups of students.

At the end of this booklet are four general grading rubrics for written and oral presentations, visual displays, and models. There is also an answer key for the student page in this booklet.

Prentice Hall World Explorer offers a wide and exciting range of options to students. Use this booklet to help you take advantage of those options.

Discovery Activities About the United States and Canada

Find Geo Cleo

Directions: Use this worksheet to name the places that Geo Cleo describes in her postcards.

1. Whew! I've been hiking through the Rocky Mountains! Right now I'm heading south. I just crossed the Colorado River. What country am I in?

_____

2. Today I crossed the border of the United States, and I'm flying to Victoria Island in Canada. Which direction am I going?

_____

3. Now I'm on a ship. We're heading from the Gulf of St. Lawrence to the Great Lakes. What river will we travel on?

_____

Bonus!

• Write clues for three other locations in the United States or Canada. Trade them with a partner and try to figure out each other's locations.

_____

_____

_____

Activities and Projects

Discovery Activities About the United States and Canada

Investigate Land Use in the United States and Canada

Directions: Use this worksheet to complete the land use activity in your textbook Activity Atlas.

1. How many different types of land use are identified on the map?

   _____

2. Which is the most common use of the land in Canada? In the United States?

   _____

3. Compare the use of land in the eastern half of the United States to that in the western half. What are the main differences?

   _____

   _____

   _____

   _____

   ### Bonus!

   - Which is the most common use of land where you live? Which is the second-most common use of land? What factors do you think have helped make this true?

     _____

     _____

     _____

Discovery Activities About the United States and Canada

Investigate the Climates of the United States and Canada

Directions: Look at the climate maps of the United States and Canada in your text-book Activity Atlas. In the space provided, answer questions about climates in both countries.

1. How many different types of climate regions are there in the United States and Canada?

_____

2. Do the climates seem to change more from east to west or from north to south?

_____

3. Which of the two countries has a region of humid subtropical climate?

_____

4. Which country has the biggest area of subarctic climate?

_____

Bonus!

- Choose six major cities in the United States and Canada and compare their climates. Be sure to choose cities in very different locations. Draw conclusions about how the location of each city affects its climate.

_____

_____

- Choose a large mountain range, such as the Rocky Mountains, the Sierra Nevada, or the Cascades. Pick one city on the east side of the range and one on the west side of the range. Compare the annual rainfall in the two locations.

_____

_____

Activities and Projects

Making a Model River

Directions: Use this worksheet to answer questions and record results as you do the Activity Shop Lab in your textbook.

Procedure

Step One states that you will make a model river in a box of sand. Do you think the river will flow in a straight line or wind back and forth? Will the channel of the river be shallow or deep? Will the channel be the same along the whole length of the river or will it change?

_____

Observations

1. How did the shape and size of your river compare with the way you predicted it would look in Step One?

    _____

2. What happened to the sand in the river's channel?

    _____

3. Describe the shape made in the sand as your river deposited its sediment near the drainage notch.

    _____

    _____

Analysis and Conclusion

1. What factors influenced the form your river took?

    _____

2. How does increased water flow affect the size and shape of your river?

    _____

3. Explain why knowledge of how rivers behave is important to city planners, farmers, boaters, and people who live near rivers.

    _____

    _____

Transtortation

Directions: Use this worksheet as you do the Activity Shop Interdisciplinary in your textbook.

I. Find the Routes

Use the lines below to name different kinds of roads and paths in your community and describe their locations. Then draw your map on another page.

a. footpaths or bicycle paths _____

b. roads _____

c. freeways _____

d. other trails _____

2. Do a Sailboat Study

Use a separate sheet of paper to sketch ideas for your sailboat design. Make a list of the materials you will need.

3. Calculate Travel Times

Use the lines below to give the average speed in miles per hour for each method of transportation.

a. 1800 stagecoach and horseback _____

b. 1860 passenger train _____

c. 1930 passenger train _____

d. 1950 automobile _____

e. passenger jet, today _____

4. Sing Some Transportation Songs

a. transportation songs I know _____

_____

b. new transportation songs I learned _____

_____

BOOK PROJECT

THE **UNITED STATES** AND **CANADA**

Write a Children's Book

A. Choosing a Topic

How will you choose a topic? Writers usually enjoy writing about things that really interest them. What stories, people, events, geographic locations, inventions, or ideas from the book did you think were amazing? As you consider topics, don't forget that you will be writing for a younger audience. Which topic might interest younger students?

You can use the chart below to write your topic ideas for a children's book. Think of a variety of topics to begin with. Then choose the one you think would work best for younger children.

Topic Ideas for a Children's Book

Topic	Is This Good for Younger Readers?

Use the information in the chart to organize the facts and information that will go into your book.

Write a Children's Book *(continued)*

B. Organizing Your Book

Now that you have chosen a topic, you can take notes and gather information. You might want to go to the library for the information you need. Divide the material into main ideas and details. Be sure to use clear and simple language, and to keep your ideas focused and brief. You can include drawings and magazine photographs.

Use the chart below to record main ideas and details that you will include in your book.

My Children's Book Outline

Main Idea 1: _____
Details:

    a.

    b.

    c.

Main Idea 2: _____
Details:

    a.

    b.

    c.

Main Idea 3: _____
Details:

    a.

    b.

    c.

Use the facts in the chart to organize the events in your story.

Activities and Projects

Write a Children's Book *(continued)*

C. Designing the Illustrations and Cover

You will need illustrations and a cover for your book. You can either find photographs in magazines or create the images yourself. Think about images that will appeal to younger readers. The images should go well with what you have written and help explain the events you have described. The cover should be colorful and include a title. It should also contain an image that comes from an important part of the story. You can use the boxes below to sketch ideas for the illustrations and the cover.

Ideas for the Illustrations

Ideas for the Cover

When you have finished sketching, create the illustrations and the cover on other sheets of paper.

Set Up a Weather Station

THE UNITED STATES AND CANADA

A. Daily Temperature Log

You are going to set up a weather station. Record the temperature, the rainfall, and the wind direction for each day. Measure each day's rainfall by placing a container outside in an open area. The container should be heavy or protected so that it will not blow away during a storm. Take your measurements at the same time and place each day. Be sure that no water from other sources can fall into the container. After you take your measurement, empty the container and place it back in its spot. It is important that you measure carefully and keep accurate records of your findings.

To determine wind direction, tie a plastic grocery bag to a pole or a stick. If you cannot do this, study your school or town flag. Wind direction is the direction from which the wind is blowing. This will be the opposite of the direction your bag or flag points to.

Use the chart below to record the temperature, amount of rainfall, and the wind direction for each day. Continue the chart on another sheet of paper if necessary.

Weather Log for My Community

Date	Time	Temperature	Precipitation (in inches)	Wind Direction

Use the information on the chart to create graphs that will show your local readings.

Name _____ Class _____ Date _____

Set Up a Weather Station *(continued)*

B. Recording Information About Weather in Other Places

Look in the newspaper for information about the weather in other parts
of the United States and Canada. You may also be able to find weather
information by watching weather reports on television. If you have
access to the Internet, you may look for weather information there.

Use the chart below to record your research.

Weather Log for the United States and Canada

Location	Date	High and Low Temperatures	Precipitation (in inches)	Wind Direction

Use the information in the chart to compare the weather in other parts
of the United States and Canada with the weather in your area.

Set Up a Weather Station *(continued)*

C. Creating Graphs

Now that you have gathered weather information, think about how you will graph each type of information. For example, which type of graph below would you choose to record daily temperatures? Which would work well for rainfall? Which one would work best for comparing information in two places? When you have completed your graphs, compare your findings with the climate map in the Activity Atlas.

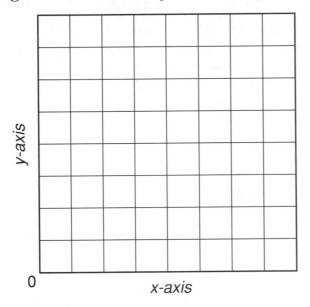

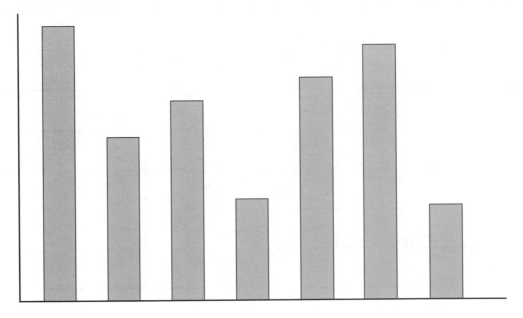

Activities and Projects

▶ **BOOK PROJECT**

THE UNITED STATES AND CANADA

Make a Time Line of Local History

A. The History of Your Community

Use books and articles from the library to find information about the history of your community. You might also talk to people whose families have lived here for a long time. They may be able to tell you about important events that you might not find in books. As you gather information, keep track of events, their dates, and your source for each piece of information.

You can use the chart below to record information about the history of your community. You may want to write a key word, symbol, or short phrase for each event. For example, if one of your events is a new train station, you might draw a train as a symbol. Use another sheet of paper if you need more space. This chart can help you arrange events in time.

Important Events

Event Key	Date	What Happened?	Where?	Source of Information

Make a Time Line
of Local History *(continued)*

B. Organizing History

Now that you have found historic events, you will need to arrange them in chronological order. If you are working with a group, begin by discussing which events you think should be included. Use the chart below to list the events in order of their occurrence. Use the key words or symbols to save time while you identify the events. Work carefully to be sure you are using the correct dates and that events are in the right order.

Event	Date

Use the information on the chart when you make your time line.

Make a Time Line of Local History *(continued)*

C. Making the Time Line

Now that all of the events are in order, you are ready to make your time line.

Materials

pencils, pens
markers, paints
photographs of historic events (optional)
large sheet of paper
ruler, yardstick, or straightedge

Procedure

1. Begin by choosing the size for your time line. If possible, make it several feet long. Then figure out how many years your time line covers. To determine the scale for your time line, divide the total number of years by the length of the line. For example, if your time line covers 240 years and is four feet long, each foot will equal 60 years. Each inch will equal five years.

2. Once you have determined the scale, use a ruler or straightedge to make marks on the line. Then write in the years. Use a scale that works with the events you have. For example, if most of the events took place during the last 40 years, your time line should focus on a shorter period of time. Then you will have enough room to include all of the events.

3. Once you have created the time line, fill in the events. Write a very short description of each event, and be sure to include an illustration or a photograph.

4. Display your time line with others from the class. Compare them and discuss how they are similar and different.

Create a Diorama

A. Choosing an Area

Which region will you use for your diorama? Will you include both the United States and Canada, or will you choose a smaller area? Either way, you will need to list the physical landmarks that you will show. These might include mountain ranges, forests, valleys, rivers, or large bodies of water. Remember, your diorama is representing a physical map. Note any large cities or other important points of interest that should be shown. As you read through the text, make note of locations or regions that you might like to use for this project. Write down details about the area that you can use for your diorama. You might also look in library books and other sources to learn more.

Use the chart below to record information for the diorama. Remember, if you choose a large area, you will only be able to include large details. If you cover a smaller area, you can add more specific details.

Diorama Details

Area or Region	Major Landforms	Cities	Other Points of Interest

Use the chart to help plan and build your diorama.

BOOK PROJECT

THE UNITED STATES AND CANADA

Create a Diorama *(continued)*

B. Making a Key

Since you will be using symbols on your diorama, you will need to make a key that explains them. Think of all the things that you would like your diorama to show. For example, it can include major cities, goods and products that are manufactured in the area, recreational areas, natural resources, national forests, transportation routes, and farmland. You can use the chart below to record the details you wish to include. Follow the example given. Invent and record a map symbol for each item.

Map Symbols for the Diorama

Item	Map Symbol
ski area	miniature skier painted on cardboard

Use the symbols in the chart in appropriate places on the diorama. Then create a key that clearly explains each symbol.

Create a Diorama *(continued)*

C. Making a Diorama

Here are some suggestions for making your diorama.

Materials

large sheets of paper
clay or dough
paints or markers
oak tag or cardboard
craft sticks
twigs
rocks
miniature buildings
box or container for the diorama
overhead projector (optional)

Procedure

1. Begin by copying onto a large sheet of paper the outlines of the region you will show. Find a map of the area to draw from. Work carefully to make the outlines as accurate as possible. If you have an overhead projector, you might use it to trace the map.

2. When the outline is finished, place it on a flat surface. Add materials to build the landforms and contours of your map. You may want to work in pairs or small groups. In this way, you can help each other create an accurate model.

3. Add symbols to the scene, such as miniature houses to represent cities or animals to represent livestock farms. Decide how to paint the map. For example, you might paint all rivers and bodies of water blue. Large forests could be green, and deserts or arid lands a sandy color. Carefully write the names of major cities, mountains, rivers, and bodies of water. Place the key where it can be seen easily.

4. When the diorama is finished, share it with other students. Compare the different dioramas and talk about the things that make each one unique and interesting.

COOPERATIVE LEARNING ACTIVITY

CHAPTER
1

THE UNITED STATES AND CANADA
Physical Geography

Creating Travel Posters for National Parks

The national park committees of Canada and the United States have asked your design team to create a series of four travel posters to attract visitors to their national parks. In this activity, your team will choose four parks and find out more about them. Then your team will create a poster for each park that tells with photographs, illustrations, and captions why people should visit there.

Background

The United States and Canada contain some of the most magnificent scenery in the world. Recognizing the value of wild lands, both countries have taken steps to preserve some of their scenic wonders. They have done this by creating national parks.

National parks are lands that are protected from development by the governments of the United States and Canada. These parks attract millions of visitors each year. National parks have been established for a variety of reasons. The most common is scenic beauty. Parks such as Yosemite, Banff, and Acadia are filled with wonderful geographic features. Other parks are protected for their historic, scientific, or recreational assets. National parks provide a wealth of activities for young and old alike. Camping, fishing, hiking, boating, whale-watching, and mountain climbing are just a few. Some national parks are huge. Others are quite small.

Procedure

1. **Choose parks.** Read all the steps in this project. Decide with your group what tasks are involved and what each team member will be responsible for. You may wish to have one designer and one writer for each poster. Then work together to find a list of national parks and their locations in the United States and Canada. Choose four parks as subjects for posters. As you do your research, you will find out more about each park.

2. **Find out about national parks.** Work with your team to look in the library for photographs and information about national parks. You may find books about individual parks. You can also probably find good materials in books about the states or provinces where parks are located.

3. **Design your posters.** When your group has gathered photographs and information, meet again to discuss the subjects of your posters. Designers and writers can work together to come up with slogans as well as visual images for each poster. Think of images that strongly express what is particularly beautiful about each park. What things attract visitors each year? Is there an image that you can create that is unusual? For example, most everyone knows that Yellowstone has geysers and bears. How might you combine these images in one design?

When you have finished the designs, make the posters. Some group members can create the artwork, while others work on captions and information. Be sure that all writing is easy to read and easy to understand.

4. **Display your posters.** You can put on a national park travel fair. Display the posters on the classroom walls. Look at all the different designs and compare them. Which would you like to visit? Discuss the different parks.

Activities and Projects

THE UNITED STATES AND CANADA
Physical Geography

Creating Travel Posters for National Parks

Content Objectives
- Students will learn more about geographic features in the United States and Canada.
- Students will gain a deeper understanding of the purposes of national parks.

Skill Objectives
- Using regional and route maps
- Reading actively
- Locating information
- Organizing information

Advance Preparation
Gather the following materials:
- information/brochures on national parks, travel magazines
- poster paper
- pencils, markers, pens, paints
- scissors and glue

Suggested group size: eight students

Suggested time: 20 minutes for planning; 40 minutes for researching information and designing the posters; 40 minutes for creating the posters; 40 minutes for displaying and discussing the work

Procedure
Assign students to groups of eight. Distribute student pages and have students begin to work on the project. You may wish to give a copy of the rubric for posters to each group.

You may want to have students choose some national parks and call or write for information. If so, this should be done in advance. Or you might select a dozen parks from which they can choose.

You may wish to ask families to share any photographs or postcards of national parks that they may have. Students can use these for graphic ideas.

When students have finished their posters, discuss them with the class. You may wish to use these questions:

- What did you find out about national parks?
- What did you learn about designing and creating a poster?
- How did your team organize this project? Who did what?

THE UNITED STATES AND CANADA
Physical Geography

Posters will be evaluated according to the following rubric.

Rubric for Posters

	Awesome	Admirable	Acceptable
Research	Students locate a great deal of interesting information about four national parks in the United States and Canada. They find many sources, including photographs and postcards from friends and family members as well as articles and books.	Students locate information about national parks in the United States and Canada. The information includes ideas for visuals from brochures and magazines.	Students locate some information about national parks.
Presentation	Posters are made with great care. They include photographs and illustrations that are beautiful and catch the eye. Each poster gives a strong sense of the national park.	Posters are attractive. They include photographs and illustrations, and each gives a sense of the national park.	Posters include photographs and illustrations.
Captions and Information	Posters contain catchy titles and interesting facts about the park. All writing is extremely neat and colorful.	Posters contain interesting facts about the park. Writing is neat and easy to read.	Posters contain facts about the parks.
Teamwork	Work is shared by all team members. The organization is efficient and makes use of the talents of each individual.	All members participate in producing posters. However, the group could make better use of the talents of some members.	All members participate.

Activities and Projects

COOPERATIVE LEARNING ACTIVITY

CHAPTER
2

THE UNITED STATES AND CANADA
Shaped by History

Presenting an Oral Biography

As you read the text, keep track of people that you think are particularly interesting or exciting. Write notes on people who appeal to you in a journal or other place. Every person who is mentioned in the history of the United States and Canada has a unique and fascinating story. Whether it is Thomas Jefferson, Harriet Beecher Stowe, Mary "Mother" Jones, or Louis Papineau, there is much more you can learn about them. In this activity, you will work with a group to present an oral biography to the class about a person in American or Canadian history.

Background

One reason to study history is to learn more about ourselves. When you really look at a person's life, you will likely discover things that you can use in your own life. In some cases, you may be inspired by someone's courage. In others, you may learn from another person's mistakes. Though many things—such as technology—do change over the years, human beings have often had to deal with similar challenges century after century. As your team looks closely at the lives of people from the past, you will be surprised at what you discover.

Procedure

1. **Choose a subject.** Read all the steps in this project. Then meet with your group to divide the tasks. Work together to choose the subject of your report. Each group member can name the people that he or she found most interesting and explain why. When your group has discussed several people, vote or otherwise decide on whom to choose.

2. **Research your person.** Use the library to find books, articles, or videos about your person. If you have access to the Internet, search there as well. Work together to research different aspects of the person's life. For example, one or two people might concentrate on your subject's childhood. Others could focus on important events in your person's life.

3. **Write the report.** Once your team members have gathered information, your group can meet again and begin writing your subject's biography. The first step is to organize your ideas in a logical manner. A good way is to sort out the main ideas you wish to communicate. Then for each main idea, you can write several details. Try to include stories that bring the person to life. Your group can use the chart below to record main ideas and details. Use another sheet of paper if necessary.

Main Idea 1: _____

Details:

    a.

    b.

    c.

Main Idea 2: _____

Details:

    a.

    b.

    c.

Main Idea 3: _____

Details:

    a.

    b.

    c.

Use the information in the chart to write the biography. Remember, your team will present it to the class. Decide who will speak each part. Some group members can collect illustrations, photographs, or maps to help give a strong impression of the person, events, and historic time.

4. **Give your report.** When your group has finished writing, decide on the order of speakers. Speak slowly and clearly. Take time to look at your audience as you share what you know. Try to communicate the enthusiasm you feel about your subject. Let people know why this person's life is important and interesting to us today. Don't be afraid to use humor.

Activities and Projects

THE UNITED STATES AND CANADA
Shaped by History

Content Objectives
- Students will learn about the history of the United States and Canada.
- Students will gain a deeper understanding of a historic figure.

Skill Objectives
- Reading actively
- Locating information
- Organizing information
- Speaking to an audience

Advance Preparation
Gather biographies and other good sources of historic information.

Suggested group size: six students

Suggested time: 20 minutes for planning; 40 minutes for researching information (you may wish to assign research and writing as homework); 40 minutes for organizing and writing the report; 40 minutes for giving reports and for discussion

Procedure
Assign class members to groups of six. Distribute student pages and have students begin to work on the project. You may wish to give a copy of the rubric for oral reports to each group.

If possible, help students find letters, journals, news articles, and other primary sources. Invite them to choose people that are not well known to everyone. Students may be pleasantly surprised to discover some new historic figures.

When students have given their reports, invite them to discuss each one. You might use these questions to begin the discussion:
- Why did you choose the person you did?
- What did you find out about another time period that you did not know before?
- Are there things you learned that you think could be helpful in your own life? What are they?
- How did members of your team work together? Describe how you assigned tasks to team members.

THE UNITED STATES AND CANADA
Shaped by History

Oral reports will be evaluated according to the following rubric.

Rubric for Oral Reports

	Awesome	Admirable	Acceptable
Research	Students use many different sources of information. They locate a great variety of information on the topic and are able to bring the person to life. They also include illustrations, photographs, maps, and other items.	Students use many sources of information. They locate interesting facts and illustrations on their topic.	Students find some information about their topic.
Writing the Report	Writing is very well organized, descriptive, and easy to understand. Students use quotations from their subjects to make the report lively. The writing communicates enthusiasm and excitement for the topic.	Writing is clear and well organized. Students describe events in a logical order and with enthusiasm.	Writing is clear and easy to understand.
Presentation	Students speak clearly and are easy to understand. They use a lively tone and engage the audience. They include humor when appropriate and keep the audience's attention throughout their talk.	Students are easy to understand. They engage the audience and have its attention.	Students can be understood. They look at the audience from time to time.
Teamwork	Groups plan tasks wisely. They use the talents and contributions of each member. All group members take responsibility for the final product.	Group members share information and offer feedback during all stages of the project.	All team members participate.

Activities and Projects

Cultures of the United States and Canada

Producing a Concert

Many people in the United States and Canada are immigrants, or are descended from immigrants. Each immigrant group brings with it its own cultural heritage. As people from different cultural backgrounds meet, their ideas, traditions, languages, and arts mix in new and wonderful ways. A great variety of music is found in the United States and Canada. In this activity, you will work with a team to find out more about a particular style of traditional music. Then you will work together to produce a concert that shares this music with other members of your class.

Background

If you travel around the United States and Canada, you can find examples of local musical styles. You can hear Cajun music in Louisiana, southwest border music in Texas, African American blues in the South, Native American ceremonial music in Arizona, Jewish klezmer music in New York City, and English ballads in Appalachia and New England. In some places, these are traditional styles that have not changed for many, many years. For example, in parts of Nova Scotia you can hear people playing Scottish fiddle music as it has been played for hundreds of years. Musicians from Scotland say that this music has changed more in their own country than in Canada. As communication has improved, many of these regional and ethnic styles have mixed to form new kinds of music. Pop, rock, and jazz are forms that draw on a wide variety of styles. When you learn about some traditional styles, you may notice that they sound familiar and have been used in music that you listen to.

Procedure

1. **Choose a musical style.** Read all the steps in this project. Then meet with your group to plan how you will do this project. You may wish to do some general research and then meet again to discuss a type of music that interests you. Choose a musical style or an ethnic group from Canada or the United States. You might want to suggest to the group music from your own cultural heritage. Ask your teacher, librarian, or local music store for advice about finding recordings.

2. **Locate recordings and information.** Once you have chosen the music you want to explore, look for books and articles about the people who make the music. You can decide with your team how to share the work. Learn how the music is used, who plays it, the common instruments, and popular songs. Notice the song lyrics. Work with one or two others to find recordings of the music that you can share with the class. You can use the table below to keep notes about specific songs, instruments, and recordings.

Type of Music	Name of Song	Instruments Used	Recording

When you have finished gathering recordings and information, meet again with your group to plan the concert. You will need one or more announcers, who will tell about the music. You will also need people to create the concert tape. Bringing to class instruments from the musical style can add a lot to your presentation.

3. **Present the recordings.** Work together to present the recordings. If there is time, you might play each recording two times. You can talk about the music and its culture after the first time, and then listen again. When all the groups have finished, discuss as a class what you have noticed about how music and the cultures of the United States and Canada have mixed.

CHAPTER
3

Cultures of the United States and Canada

Producing a Concert

Content Objectives
- Students will learn about a variety of musical styles from the United States and Canada.
- Students will gain a deeper understanding of the relationship between music and the cultural heritage of a people and a nation.

Skill Objectives
- Recognizing cause and effect
- Drawing conclusions
- Writing for a purpose—explanation
- Locating information
- Organizing information

Advance Preparation
Gather the following materials:
- recordings and information about musical styles in the United States and Canada
- tape recorders

Suggested group size: six students

Suggested time: 20 minutes for planning; 40 minutes for finding recordings and information; 40 minutes for preparing the concert; 40 minutes for presenting and discussing the recordings

Procedure
Divide the class into groups of six. Distribute student pages and have students begin to work on the project. You may wish to give a copy of the rubric for music presentations to each group.

Before students listen to the music, point out the value of listening to music without distractions. Explain that with each listening, they will hear more details in the music.

You may need to help students locate recordings. Local record stores may be willing to help you with this. Many libraries have recordings available as well.

When students have presented their music, ask them to discuss what they have learned. If you like, use these questions to begin:
- What have you learned about music in the United States and Canada?
- What were your favorite pieces of music? Why? What was the most unusual music you heard?
- What did the musical examples tell you about the cultures they are part of?
- How did your group prepare its concert?

Cultures of the United States and Canada

Music presentations will be evaluated according to the following rubric.

Rubric for Music Presentations

	Awesome	Admirable	Acceptable
Research	Students find many recordings and extensive information about a musical style and its culture. They locate photographs, interviews with musicians, and instruments.	Students find recordings and information about the music and its culture. They locate photographs and instruments.	Students find some recordings and information about the music and its culture.
Writing the Text	The writing is full of interesting facts that clearly explain how the music is used, by whom, and for what purpose or purposes. Students discuss each musical example and point out how it expresses its cultural heritage. Students are able to show how the style has contributed to other musical styles or forms.	The writing contains interesting facts about the music and the people who play it. Each musical example is explained clearly and in detail.	The writing contains some information about the music and its culture.
Presentation	Presentations are extremely well organized. Students play recordings and speak clearly and with enthusiasm about each one. They keep the attention of their listeners with a lively presentation.	Presentations are well organized. Students speak clearly and with enthusiasm.	Presentations are organized. Students play recordings and explain them.
Teamwork	Groups work well together. They are excited about the project and share jobs equally.	Groups work well together. They support each other's work.	Group members work together and complete the project.

Activities and Projects

COOPERATIVE LEARNING ACTIVITY

CHAPTER 4

Exploring the United States

Simulation: Town Meeting on Water Use

In many arid regions of California and the Southwest, people discuss how they should use water. Many arid areas get their water from far-away sources. In communities throughout arid parts of the West, citizens express different opinions about how water resources should be used and protected. In this activity, you will hold a "town meeting," in which you as citizens will debate how water should be used.

Background

In arid parts of states in the West, many people working on desert farms or living in new communities must get water from sources in other states. Other communities dig deep wells that tap into large underground deposits of water called aquifers. Some geologists warn that once aquifers are used up, that source of water might be gone forever.

Your group and other groups living in your community have been invited to discuss water use at a town meeting. You live in an arid region, such as Phoenix, Arizona; Las Vegas, Nevada; or Los Angeles, California. The following groups of people are part of your community: those who support growth through rapid development of homes, offices, and shopping centers; those who want to limit development; farmers who need water for their crops; and geologists who are concerned about the effects of wells, canals, dams on rivers, and aquifers.

The largest water users in your area are farmers. However, people also use water for gardens, lawns, and swimming pools. Your area is growing very rapidly.

Procedure

1. **Make a plan.** Your teacher will assign you to a team and tell your team which community group it will represent. Your teacher may also choose a particular city or area that you will study. Read all the steps in this project. Then meet with your team to plan. Decide how you will divide up the responsibility for presenting a statement at the town meeting. You may decide to make two students responsible for getting information on how aquifers, wells, dams, and canals work. Another pair of students can find out about natural sources of water in your area. Another can find information about water policies in the location you are studying. Two people will organize information and write notes for the presentation. Your team may want to choose one spokesperson or divide the presentation among its members.

2. **Look for information.** Look in atlases, newspapers, magazines, and other sources for information about water use in arid regions. As you are locating information, you should keep in mind your group's opinion. For example, if your team is representing farmers, members can search for articles about irrigation or farming as well as information about the value of farms and farm products to a region. Or, if you are representing development, find out how growth affects the local economy. Ask your teacher or librarian for help.

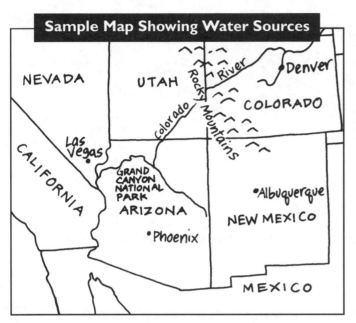

Sample Map Showing Water Sources

Sample Data

	(in thousands)
Potatoes=	$28,728
Oats =	$5,091
Corn =	$383,565
Watermelons=	$72,038
Peppers=	$21,870

3. **Write your point of view.** Use your information to write a statement. You may want to have each group member write and read one part. Be sure that each statement is strong and is supported by facts. Decide on the best order for stating your points.

4. **Hold a town meeting.** When all the teams are ready, it's time for the town meeting. Your teacher may act as the meeting's leader, or may decide to have a student lead the meeting. It is very important to listen carefully as all classmates speak. Don't interrupt—if you disagree with something you hear, write notes so you can respond when the speaker has finished. After each team has presented its points, try to come up with a plan for water use in your community.

Activities and Projects

Exploring the United States

Town Meeting on Water Use

Content Objectives

- Students will find out more about how water is delivered to dry areas.
- Students will explore how water use affects water resources.
- Students will learn more about the process of participating in a town meeting.

Skill Objectives

- Expressing problems clearly
- Locating information
- Identifying central issues
- Identifying cause and effect
- Writing for a purpose—oral report

Advance Preparation

Gather information on irrigation methods and water use in arid regions.

Suggested group size: eight students

Suggested time: 20 minutes for planning; 40 minutes for researching information; 60 minutes for sharing information and writing oral reports; 40 minutes for a town meeting

Procedure

Have students work in groups of eight. Assign each team of students a particular group in the community. You may wish to decide on a particular area of the country as the location for the community. Distribute student pages and have students read through the steps in the project. You may wish to give a copy of the rubric for statements to each group.

Point out that town meetings are often an important part of local government. Ask students who have attended town meetings to describe them. You may wish to engage students in a general discussion about water use in your area of the country.

When it's time for the town meeting, you may wish to act as moderator. Remind students to listen carefully to each speaker. Point out that they will have an opportunity to respond during the general discussion. During discussion, see if students can come to an agreement about water use. You may use the following questions.

- How is water delivered to arid regions?
- How is the water supply affected by human needs, such as farming and development?
- How can communities protect their water sources and meet other needs?
- What suggestions would you make for using water in the community?

Exploring the United States

Oral presentations will be evaluated according to the following rubric.

Rubric for Statements

Activities and Projects

	Awesome	Admirable	Acceptable
Research	Students use a variety of appropriate sources to find out how irrigation systems work. Their research helps them understand how water use affects resources. They find information that helps them speak concretely and wisely about water use in the area under discussion.	Students find several good sources of information about how water is used in a particular area. Their research helps them support the opinions of the community group they represent.	Students locate a few sources of information about water use and its effects.
Writing	Statements are clear, concise, and to the point. They are very well organized and strongly express the point of view. Each point is backed up with facts. They include visuals where appropriate.	Statements are clear and to the point. They are well organized and do a good job of expressing the point of view.	Statements are well organized and express the point of view.
Presentation	Students speak with ease. They are easy to understand and keep the attention of the audience. Students listen carefully when not speaking.	Students speak clearly and can be understood. They keep the audience's attention.	Students speak clearly and can be understood.
Teamwork	Students make an excellent team. They help each other and share all the work equally. They enjoy working together even when working out differences.	Students make a good team. They share the project well.	Students work as a team and share most of the work.

CHAPTER
5

Exploring Canada

Writing a Newspaper Feature

More than 80 percent of the population of Quebec speaks French as its primary language. French Canadians live throughout other provinces in Canada as well. Since 1977, French is the only language used in Quebec government, commerce, and some schools. In this activity, your group will learn more about the history, culture, and lives of French Canadians and the province of Quebec. Then the people in your group will work together to write newspaper features about different aspects of French Canadian life. Finally, all the groups will work together to arrange the features and publish a special section on Quebec.

Background

When Britain gained control of Canada after the French and Indian War, French settlers were surrounded by English-speaking colonists. The first British governors allowed the French in Quebec to keep their language, customs, and religion. However, Britain and France had had a long history of conflict. They had competed for territory in the Americas, and fought each other on European battlefields as well. To this day, many French Canadians feel it is important to maintain their French cultural heritage. Now Canada is a bilingual country, with both French and English as official languages.

Procedure

1. **Choose topics for your features.** Read all the steps in this project. Meet with your team to decide what kinds of articles you will write. You might look at the Sunday edition of a newspaper and note the types of articles you find. Newspapers are usually divided into local, national, and international news articles; business news; the arts; sports; editorials; letters; and classified ads. You may want to organize your team so that the whole group plans the articles; then individuals research and write news, art, sports, and travel articles. You may want to have another person act as editor to edit the articles, suggest photographs or art, and write headlines.

2. **Organize information.** As team members finish their research, your team may want to meet again to decide which ideas you think would make the best feature articles.

Feature Topic	Source	Reporter

3. **Write your feature articles.** Before you write articles, read some features from newspapers to see how different kinds of articles are written. If you want, you can include editorials as well as letters that might appear in a Quebec newspaper. Remember to write a headline for each article.

4. **Publish the paper.** When teams have finished the articles, your team can work with other groups to assemble the paper. You may be able to design it on a computer.

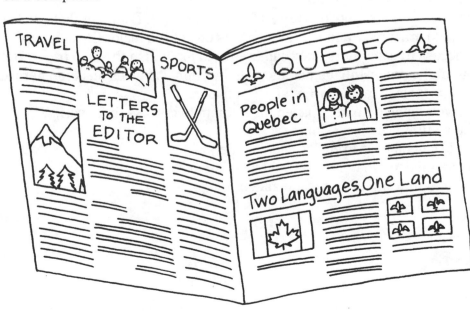

Activities and Projects

Exploring Canada

Writing a Newspaper Feature

Content Objectives
- Students will learn more about French Canadian culture and the province of Quebec.
- Students will gain a deeper understanding about newspaper feature articles.

Skill Objectives
- Reading actively
- Writing for a purpose—newspaper articles and editorials
- Locating information
- Organizing information

Advance Preparation
Gather Sunday editions of newspapers, including travel sections, and travel brochures on locations in Quebec.

Suggested group size: eight students

Suggested time: 20 minutes for planning; 90 minutes for researching, organizing, and writing articles; 60 minutes for putting the newspaper together

Procedure
Assign students to groups and distribute student pages. You may wish to give a copy of the rubric for newspaper articles to each group.

Encourage students to find a variety of sources for their articles. Point out that Quebec contains both urban and rural areas, and that Montreal is one of the major Canadian cities.

If students have access to computers, they can use them to publish the final paper. Help them as needed. You might suggest that students write individual articles on computers and then paste articles and visuals onto one larger sheet of paper.

When students have finished the newspaper, invite them to discuss their work. The following questions may help stimulate discussion:
- What have you learned about French Canadian life?
- If you could visit Quebec, what places would you like to see?
- How did it help you to work as part of a team on this project?

Exploring Canada

Articles will be evaluated according to the following rubric.

Rubric for Newspaper Articles

	Awesome	Admirable	Acceptable
Research	Students find information about many interesting subjects. They obtain information from a wide variety of sources. They collect articles over several days.	Students find many topics for articles.	Students find some topics for articles.
Writing the Articles	Articles are clearly written. They tell who, what, where, when, and how about the topics. Writing is lively, interesting, and easy to understand. Each article has a headline that explains the topic and catches the reader's attention.	Articles are well written and well organized. They tell who, what, where, when, and how about each topic. Articles have interesting headlines that attract the reader's attention and include vivid language.	Articles are clearly written. Headlines contain useful information.
Creating the Newspaper	Newspapers are laid out with great attention to the sizes and placement of the various elements. Visuals add information and interest to the articles.	Newspapers are laid out neatly and attractively. The sizes of headlines and visuals are appropriate.	Newspapers are laid out neatly, but they may not clearly connect visuals with the articles.
Teamwork	Groups work very well as a team. They share information. Each member performs his or her role. The editor provides leadership. All members cooperate to produce a high-quality newspaper.	Groups work as a team and share the jobs equally. The editor shows leadership.	All members participate. However, the work is not evenly shared.

Activities and Projects

Assessment of a Written Presentation

Use this rubric to assess students' essays, written reports, and any other written materials, such as captions for maps or diagrams.

	Awesome	Admirable	Acceptable	Unacceptable
Creativity	The presentation has a highly interesting topic that is conveyed in an extremely engaging manner. Students include several original ideas, including some that are unusual.	The presentation has an interesting topic that is conveyed in an engaging manner. Students include one or two original ideas.	The presentation has an appropriate topic that is conveyed with a few interesting details.	The topic of the presentation may be inappropriate, and/or students use only obvious examples to back up their main points.
Content	The presentation includes excellent information gathered from a variety of sources. All the elements, such as captions for illustrations and the title, are concise and informative.	The presentation includes good information gathered from three or four sources. The project's general conclusions are supported by the data presented.	The information in the presentation is relevant, but students may have used only two reference sources.	The information in the presentation may not be relevant to the topic, and/or students use only one reference source, resulting in a limited understanding of the subject.
Organization	The information is very well organized and conveyed in a logical order. Each main point is supported by interesting and appropriate details.	The information is conveyed in a logical order, and the report is easy to follow and understand.	The information is presented in a logical order, and the supporting details almost always follow the appropriate main points.	The information is not presented logically, and supporting details are either missing or misplaced.
Spelling, Grammar, and Neatness	The written material is very neat and attractively presented. Students use correct spelling and grammar.	The written material is attractive and neat. Students make very few spelling or grammatical errors.	The written material is legible. Students make a few spelling and grammatical errors.	The written material is mostly legible, but some sections are very hard to read. Students make several spelling and grammatical errors.

Assessment of an Oral Presentation

Use this rubric to assess students' oral reports and their public speaking skills.

	Awesome	Admirable	Acceptable	Unacceptable
Content	The presentation is highly persuasive and informative. Students emphasize important information about the topic and include many fascinating details in their presentation.	The presentation is persuasive and informative. Students include pertinent information about the topic and illustrate their points with three or four interesting details.	The presentation is informative. Students convey correct information about the topic and illustrate their points with one or two details.	The presentation is somewhat or not at all informative. Some of the information in it may be incorrect. Students make only broad statements about the topic, giving few or no details.
Preparation	Students gather information from several appropriate sources. They prepare note cards to guide them as they speak and create attractive visual aids to enhance the presentation.	Students gather information from three or four sources. They prepare notes to use while they speak and create informative visual aids for the presentation.	Students gather information from one or two sources. Instead of preparing notes, they write the report word-for-word as it will be given.	Students use only one reference source to prepare for the presentation. They may be unable to complete their presentation because of lack of preparation.
Organization	The information is very well organized, logically ordered, and easy to follow. Students include interesting and appropriate examples to support their main points.	Students convey the information in a logical order, and the presentation is easy to follow and understand.	Students present the information in a logical order. Generally, the supporting details follow the main points.	The information is not presented logically, and supporting details are either missing or misplaced.
Speaking	Students are enthusiastic during the presentation. They enunciate clearly, project well, maintain eye contact with their audience, and speak in complete sentences.	Students are engaged during the presentation. They enunciate clearly, project well, and speak mostly in complete sentences.	Students present their material clearly, and try to maintain eye contact.	Students come across as disinterested during the presentation. They may be hard to understand and speak in fragmented sentences.

Activities and Projects

Assessment of a Visual Display

Use this rubric to assess students' maps, diagrams, murals, graphs, illustrated stories or articles, and any other visual displays.

	Awesome	Admirable	Acceptable	Unacceptable
Content	The display conveys accurate information from several appropriate sources. Students include excellent renditions of all the necessary elements, such as a title and a legend for a map.	The display conveys accurate information from more than one source. Students include all the necessary elements, such as clearly labeled axes on a graph.	The display conveys accurate information from a reliable source. Important elements are present and convey most of the necessary information.	The display may contain inaccurate information. Important elements, such as the legend for a map, are missing.
Creativity	Students employ a highly innovative approach to creating the display. They combine several original ideas with existing materials to create a unique display.	Students combine one or two original ideas with existing materials to create an interesting display.	Students create an informative display that includes a few interesting ideas or details.	Rather than using their own ideas to make a unique display, students copy from an existing source.
Color and Form	Elements of the display are highly attractive and compatible with other elements. Whenever possible, students use colors to convey information instead of as mere decoration.	Elements of the display are attractive and work well together. Students use colors that are appropriate to the subject matter and often convey content as well as being decorative.	Elements of the display are the correct size and in the correct places. Students pay sufficient attention to conveying content with color.	Some elements of the display may be inappropriately sized. For example, a map legend may be larger than the map itself. Colors are used haphazardly.
Drawing and Labeling	Students are very careful and neat when they render their display; for example, they use straightedges to draw lines. All necessary parts of diagrams and maps are labeled clearly.	Students carefully draw elements of their displays so that the information in them is easy to understand. They include appropriate labels wherever necessary.	Students create a generally neat and readable display. They include some good labels, most of which are easy to read.	Several elements in the display are hurriedly drawn and sloppy. Students use too few labels, or the labels do not convey the correct information.

Assessment of a Model

Use this rubric to assess students' models, dioramas, and any other three-dimensional projects.

	Awesome	Admirable	Acceptable	Unacceptable
Research	Students conduct extensive research for their model, using several appropriate sources. They gather more material than they eventually use, resulting in a high level of precision.	Students gather information from three or four appropriate and varied sources. For example, they use the Internet or magazines as well as general encyclopedias.	Students gather information from one or two appropriate sources. They may rely very heavily on only one of the sources.	Students use only one reference source to prepare their model, resulting in a limited understanding of the subject.
Content	The model is an excellent representation of the scene or phenomenon being studied. Students exhibit a thorough understanding of how the model relates to the real world.	Students use the model to accurately depict a particular scene or phenomenon. Students can explain how the model works and answer questions about their work.	Students create a model that demonstrates a particular scene or phenomenon. They mostly understand how their model relates to the real world.	The model shows a scene or demonstrates a phenomenon, but it contains errors or incongruous elements, such as a human and a dinosaur in the same scene.
Quality of Construction	The model is very sturdy and well constructed. In dioramas, glue, tape, and other such materials are hidden, resulting in a highly realistic scene.	The model is sturdy. In dioramas, construction materials, such as glue and tape, are not evident, and the scene looks realistic.	Although the model may be sturdy, construction materials, such as glue and tape, are easy to see, detracting somewhat from the realism of the scene.	Even though some parts of the model may be sturdy, other parts have fallen apart. Elements of the model have been hurriedly taped together.
Presentation	The model is highly attractive and detailed, although none of the details are extraneous. In dioramas, students render elements of the scene very realistically.	The model is attractive and includes many interesting details. Students draw and color elements of dioramas so that they are easy to understand.	The model adequately presents a scene. Most of the elements of dioramas are easy to make out or understand.	The model fails to present a scene adequately. Students pay little attention to color or shape when they make the elements of a diorama.

Activities and Projects

Answer Key

Discovery Activities About the United States and Canada
ACTIVITY ATLAS

Find Geo Cleo
1. the United States
2. north
3. St. Lawrence River

Bonus!
- Answers will vary. Sample answer: I am standing on a huge volcano looking out at the sea. I am thousands of miles from California. Where am I? (Hawaii)

Investigate Land Use in the United States and Canada
1. 7
2. hunting and gathering; commercial farming
3. In the east, there is more commercial farming and manufacturing; in the west; there is more livestock raising and forestry.

Bonus!
- Students should be able to describe how the land is used where they live and give concrete reasons for their answers.

Investigate the Climates of the United States and Canada
1. 11
2. north to south
3. the United States
4. Canada

Bonus!
- Answers will vary.
- Students should observe that the rainfall is much greater on one side than on the other. For mountains in the western regions, the west side will have more annual rainfall than the east side.

Making a Model River
ACTIVITY SHOP LAB

Procedure
If the model simulates a real river, the course of the water will change in direction and depth. The water flow will depend on the river pattern created.

Observations
1. Answers will vary. Students should accurately compare their predictions with their observations.
2. Some of the sand moved along with the flow of the water.
3. The sand should form a triangular shape.

Analysis and Conclusion
1. Answers may vary. The angle of the slope and the amount of water flow are probably the two most important factors.
2. Answers may vary. Possible answers may include that the flooding of the river "banks" causes the river to widen or new branches to form.
3. Possible answers: City planners might plan a public park near a river. Farmers might assess whether a river's flow would be adequate for irrigation purposes. People who live near rivers may have flooding problems. Boaters would need to be aware that sediment can build up in certain places, which might make boating difficult or impossible.

Transportation
ACTIVITY SHOP INTERDISCIPLINARY

Answers will vary.

Answer Key

Write a Children's Book
BOOK PROJECT

A. Students should fill in the chart with ideas for their children's book topics. They should note whether each one would be good for younger readers.
B. Students should fill in the chart with facts and information for their children's book.
C. Students should use the spaces to sketch ideas for illustrations and the book cover.

Set Up a Weather Station
BOOK PROJECT

A. Students should fill in the chart with information about the weather for each day.
B. Students should fill in the chart with information about the weather in other parts of the United States and Canada.
C. Answers may vary. Accept all logical reasons for students' choices.

Make a Time Line of Local History
BOOK PROJECT

A. Students should fill in the chart with a list of important events in the history of their community. They should include the event, date, description, and source for each item.
B. Students should use the chart to arrange events in chronological order.

Create a Diorama
BOOK PROJECT

A. Students should fill in the chart with information about major landforms, cities, and other points of interest.
B. Students should fill in the chart with items they want to include in their dioramas. They should create a map symbol for each item and record it.

Activities and Projects

Tests

TEST A

THE UNITED STATES AND CANADA
Physical Geography

A. Key Terms

Directions: Complete each sentence in Column I by writing the letter of the correct term from Column II in the blank. You will not use all the terms. *(10 points)*

Column I

_____ 1. A huge, slow-moving sheet of ice is called a(n) _____ .

_____ 2. In the Arctic, a cold, dry region called the _____ is covered with snow for more than half the year.

_____ 3. The surface of _____ , which is permanently frozen subsoil, thaws only during the Arctic summer.

_____ 4. A region of flat or rolling land covered with grasses is a(n) _____ .

_____ 5. The silt that is left by rivers after a flood forms is _____ soil.

Column II

a. tundra

b. rain shadow

c. Continental Divide

d. glacier

e. alluvial

f. tributary

g. prairie

h. agribusiness

i. permafrost

B. Key Concepts

Directions: Write the letter of the correct answer or ending in each blank. *(45 points)*

_____ 6. One major landform that is found in both the United States and Canada is
    a. the Kilauea Volcano.
    b. the Rocky Mountains.
    c. the Great Basin.
    d. Mount Logan.

_____ 7. Why are the Great Lakes important to both the United States and Canada?
    a. They form the Continental Divide.
    b. They are an important link to the Pacific Ocean.
    c. They are major shipping routes.
    d. They form a boundary with Alaska.

_____ 8. How do the huge plains areas in Canada and the United States affect the way people live here?
    a. The rich soil is good for farming.
    b. The tall mountains provide lumber.
    c. The volcanic soil hardens into new land.
    d. The very rugged land makes settlement difficult.

_____ **9.** Because Canada is a long way from the Equator, much of the country has a climate that is
a. moderate. **c.** cool.
b. warm. **d.** very cold.

_____ **10.** Factors that influence the climate in both the United States and Canada include oceans, mountains, and
a. agriculture. **c.** latitude.
b. population. **d.** volcanoes.

_____ **11.** Geographers identify four major kinds of plant life in the United States and Canada: tundra, grassland, desert scrub, and
a. prairie. **c.** volcanic.
b. subtropical. **d.** forest.

_____ **12.** The major natural resources of the United States are soil, water, timber, farmland, and
a. solar energy. **c.** manufactured goods.
b. minerals. **d.** agribusinesses.

_____ **13.** Much of Canada's mineral wealth is found in the
a. Prairie Provinces. **c.** St. Lawrence Lowlands.
b. Canadian Shield. **d.** Great Lakes.

_____ **14.** The rivers of Quebec Province are used to make
a. solar energy. **c.** thermal energy.
b. hydroelectric power. **d.** petroleum.

C. Critical Thinking

Directions: Answer the following questions on the back of this paper or on a separate sheet of paper. *(20 points)*

15. Cause and Effect Consider what you have learned about the geography and climate of Canada and the United States. Why do you think the United States has 10 times more people than Canada?

16. Identifying Central Issues Imagine that you are a farmer from England who comes to Canada or the United States to live in the 1800s. In what area of Canada or the United States will you settle and start a farm? Explain your choice.

D. Skills

Directions: Use the population map below to answer the following questions. Write your answers in the blanks provided. *(25 points)*

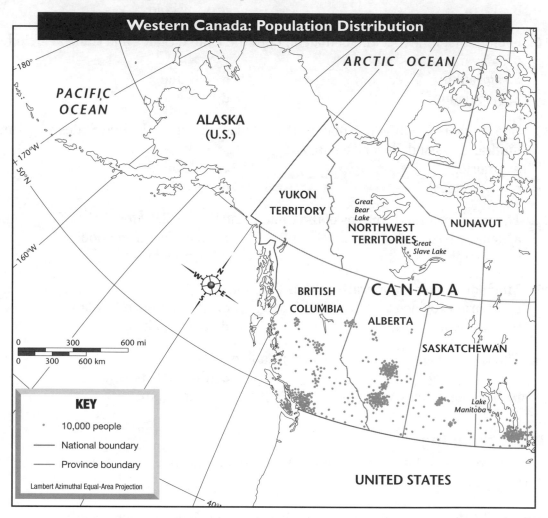

Western Canada: Population Distribution

17. What information does the title of this map provide? _____

18. How is the population represented on the map? _____

19. How many people does each symbol stand for? _____

20. Which area of western Canada has the highest population density?

    _____

21. Consider the climate and vegetation of western Canada. Why do you think so much of this region is sparsely populated?

    _____

THE UNITED STATES AND CANADA
Physical Geography

A. Key Terms

Directions: Match the definitions in Column I with the terms in Column II. Write the correct letter in each blank. You will not use all the terms. *(10 points)*

Column I

_____ 1. the boundary separating rivers flowing toward opposite sides of the continent

_____ 2. a huge, slow-moving sheet of ice

_____ 3. a region of flat or rolling land covered with tall grasses

_____ 4. watering farmland by artificial methods

_____ 5. composed of silt deposited by water

Column II

a. glacier

b. alluvial

c. Continental Divide

d. agribusiness

e. hydroelectricity

f. irrigation

g. tundra

h. tributary

i. prairie

B. Key Concepts

Directions: Write the letter of the correct answer or ending in each blank. *(45 points)*

_____ 6. How do the United States and Canada appear from outer space?
    a. as two separate countries
    b. as different continents
    c. as one landmass
    d. as a landmass divided by the Atlantic Ocean

_____ 7. The landform that lies between the Rockies and the Appalachians is
    a. a huge plains area.
    b. the St. Lawrence River.
    c. the Great Lakes.
    d. the Laurentian Highlands.

_____ 8. Why do so few people live on the land covered by the Canadian Shield?
    a. The land is too warm.
    b. The land is too rugged.
    c. The land is too dry.
    d. The land is too wet.

Tests

_____ 9. Because much of Canada is a long way from the Equator, the climate is
    a. tropical.
    b. moderate.
    c. cold.
    d. warm.

_____ 10. Which statement best compares the climates in the United States and Canada?
    a. The climate in the United States is colder than the climate in Canada.
    b. The climate in Canada is milder than the climate in the United States.
    c. There is a greater variety of climates in the United States.
    d. The climates in both countries are the same.

_____ 11. Factors that influence the climate zones in the United States and Canada include latitude, mountains, and
    a. vegetation.
    b. manufacturing.
    c. oceans.
    d. prairies.

_____ 12. Geographers identify four major kinds of plant life in the United States and Canada: desert scrub, forest, grassland, and
    a. Arctic.
    b. tundra.
    c. tropics.
    d. rain forest.

_____ 13. Where are the largest oil reserves in North America?
    a. along the eastern coast
    b. near the Great Lakes
    c. in the Canadian Shield
    d. along the northern coast of Alaska

_____ 14. Why are the Prairie Provinces and the St. Lawrence Lowlands important to the economy of Canada?
    a. They are major agricultural regions.
    b. They are major mineral regions.
    c. They are major manufacturing regions.
    d. They are major forest regions.

C. Critical Thinking

Directions: Answer the following questions on the back of this paper or on a separate sheet of paper. *(20 points)*

15. **Drawing Conclusions** Think about the waters that act as natural divisions between the United States and Canada. What conclusions can you draw about the effect of these natural divisions on the relationship between the two nations?

16. **Identifying Central Issues** If you looked down at the United States and Canada from outer space, what major landforms common to both countries would you see?

D. Skills

Directions: Use the population map below to answer the following questions. Write your answers in the blanks provided. *(25 points)*

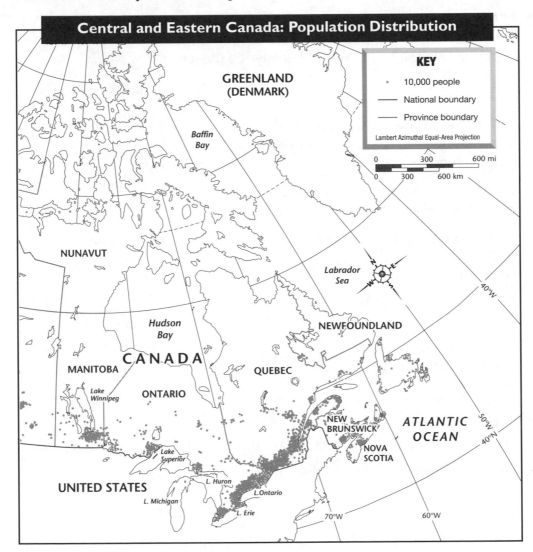

Central and Eastern Canada: Population Distribution

17. What information does the title of this map provide?

_____

18. How is the population represented on the map? _____

19. How many people does each symbol stand for? _____

20. Which area of Central and Eastern Canada has the highest population density?

_____

21. Which area of Central and Eastern Canada has the lowest population density?

_____

Name _____ Class _____ Date _____

TEST A

THE UNITED STATES AND CANADA
Shaped by History

A. Key Terms

Directions: Complete each sentence in Column I by writing the letter of the correct term from Column II in the blank. You will not use all the terms. *(10 points)*

Column I

_____ 1. Before the Revolutionary War, the American colonists decided to ____ , or refuse to buy, British goods.

_____ 2. A person who wanted to end slavery in the United States was called a(n) ____ .

_____ 3. After the Industrial Revolution, many poor immigrants joined the ____ , or supply of workers.

_____ 4. In 1867, Canada became a(n) ____ , or self-governing area.

_____ 5. When logging companies practice ____ , they cut down all the trees in an area.

Column II

a. dominion

b. clear-cutting

c. bilingual

d. boycott

e. fossil fuel

f. indigenous

g. interdependent

h. labor force

i. abolitionist

B. Key Concepts

Directions: Write the letter of the correct answer or ending in each blank. *(45 points)*

_____ 6. Some scientists think that Native Americans migrated from
   a. Europe.
   b. Asia.
   c. Spain.
   d. England.

_____ 7. What was the purpose of the United States Constitution that was approved in 1789?
   a. It set up the framework of the government.
   b. It officially ended the Revolutionary War.
   c. It inspired many colonists to fight for their independence.
   d. It demanded an end to the British tariff system.

_____ 8. Which statement best explains why the Louisiana Purchase of 1803 was important to the development of the United States?
   a. It created new taxes on imported goods.
   b. It resulted in immigration from France to the United States.
   c. It doubled the size of the country.
   d. It encouraged Native Americans to settle more land in the West.

_____ **9.** Why did some Southern states withdraw from the United States in 1860?

    a. They wanted to avoid the Civil War.

    b. They didn't believe in Manifest Destiny.

    c. They wanted to trade freely with Great Britain.

    d. They feared they would have little say in the government.

_____ **10.** What was one event that helped make the United States a world power?

    a. The country experienced the Great Depression.

    b. The country fought in World War I.

    c. The country signed the Peace of Paris.

    d. The country fought in the French and Indian War.

_____ **11.** The United States feared that the Soviets were trying to expand their power throughout the world. This fear resulted in

    a. World War II.

    b. the Cold War.

    c. World War I.

    d. the NAFTA agreement.

_____ **12.** As a result of the 1763 Treaty of Paris, Great Britain gained complete control over

    a. Newfoundland.

    b. Canada.

    c. Quebec.

    d. the United States.

_____ **13.** What was one important political result of the Canadian constitution of 1982?

    a. Quebec became an independent nation.

    b. English became the official language of Canada.

    c. Canada became completely independent.

    d. A monarchy was established in Canada.

_____ **14.** The United States and Canada have worked to solve environmental problems such as water pollution, soil erosion, and

    a. acid rain.

    b. tariffs on imported goods.

    c. free trade.

    d. the North American Free Trade Agreement.

C. Critical Thinking

Directions: Answer the following questions on the back of this paper or on a separate sheet of paper. *(20 points)*

15. Making Comparisons Explain the similarities and differences between the American Revolution and Canada's "peaceful revolution." What did each revolution accomplish?

16. Identifying Central Issues Former President John F. Kennedy, in describing the relationship between Canada and the United States, said that "economics has made us partners." Explain how the development of the St. Lawrence Seaway illustrates this economic partnership.

Tests

D. Skills

Directions: Use the diagram below to answer the following questions. Write your answers in the blanks provided. *(25 points)*

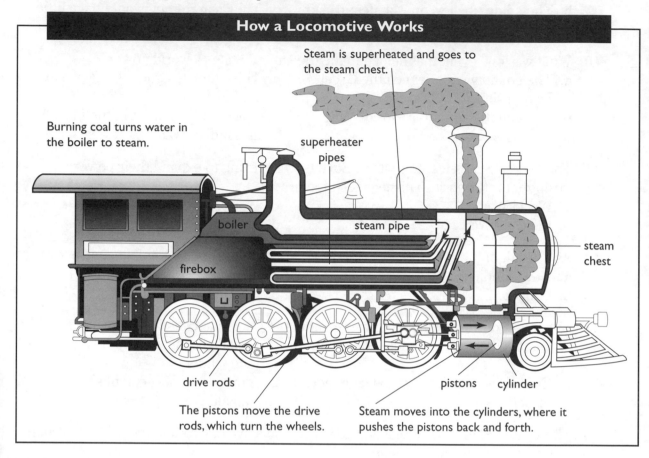

How a Locomotive Works

Steam is superheated and goes to the steam chest.

Burning coal turns water in the boiler to steam.

superheater pipes

boiler

steam pipe

steam chest

firebox

drive rods

pistons   cylinder

The pistons move the drive rods, which turn the wheels.

Steam moves into the cylinders, where it pushes the pistons back and forth.

17. What is the purpose of this diagram?

_____

18. What does the picture tell you about how a locomotive works?

_____

19. What do the labels in the diagram identify? How is movement shown?

_____

20. What are the names of three parts of a locomotive?

_____

21. How does the combination of words and pictures make this diagram a useful study tool?

_____

THE UNITED STATES AND CANADA
Shaped by History

A. Key Terms

Directions: Match the definitions in Column I with the terms in Column II. Write the correct letter in each blank. You will not use all the terms. *(10 points)*

Column I

_____ **1.** a person who has to work for a period of years to gain his or her freedom

_____ **2.** a person who moves from one country to another

_____ **3.** a form of government in which the state owns all industries

_____ **4.** a self-governing area

_____ **5.** a fee charged on an import

Column II

a. immigrant

b. bilingual

c. indentured servant

d. abolitionist

e. dominion

f. indigenous

g. communism

h. tariff

B. Key Concepts

Directions: Write the letter of the correct answer or ending in each blank. *(45 points)*

_____ **6.** Why did English settlers come to America?
   a. to find gold
   b. to become fur traders
   c. to start a new life
   d. to become missionaries

_____ **7.** Why did American colonists object to the taxes on British goods?
   a. Great Britain was boycotting American-made goods.
   b. They preferred to buy goods made in France.
   c. They were being taxed without having any representation in Parliament.
   d. They wanted to use goods made in America.

_____ **8.** How did the doctrine of Manifest Destiny in the United States affect the development of the country in the 1800s?
   a. Many Americans moved westward across the continent to settle new territories.
   b. Many Americans moved to European countries looking for work.
   c. Americans encouraged Native Americans to move eastward across the country.
   d. Americans wanted to develop the eastern coast of the United States.

Tests

_____ 9. Why were the Southern states displeased when California was admitted to the Union as a free state?
    a. Slaves were escaping from California to Canada.
    b. More slaves were needed to work on the Southern plantations.
    c. The Fugitive Slave Act would not be passed.
    d. The Southern states wanted slavery to spread into the new territories.

_____ 10. After Lincoln's election as President, why did some Southern states withdraw from the United States?
    a. to abolish slavery
    b. to found a new country
    c. to establish closer ties with Great Britain
    d. to become part of Mexico

_____ 11. How did the Industrial Revolution affect the poor in the late 1800s?
    a. The city slums emptied.
    b. Poverty was eliminated.
    c. The life of the poor did not improve.
    d. The life of the poor improved greatly.

_____ 12. The United States entered the Cold War because it was afraid of
    a. social problems in other countries.
    b. another world war with Germany and Japan.
    c. an economic decline after World War II.
    d. Soviet expansion throughout the world.

_____ 13. Under the terms of the Treaty of Paris, which country gained complete control over Canada?
    a. the United States
    b. France
    c. Spain
    d. Great Britain

_____ 14. As a result of the British North American Act of 1867, Canada had its own
    a. monarch.
    b. central government.
    c. language.
    d. economy.

C. Critical Thinking

Directions: Answer the following questions on the back of this paper or on a separate sheet of paper. *(20 points)*

15. **Identifying Central Issues** Select one of the environmental issues facing both the United States and Canada. Explain how the countries have worked together to solve this problem.

16. **Making Comparisons** Explain the similarities and differences between how the Spanish and French dealt with the indigenous peoples in North America.

D. Skills

Directions: Use the diagram below to answer the following questions. Write your answers in the blanks provided. *(25 points)*

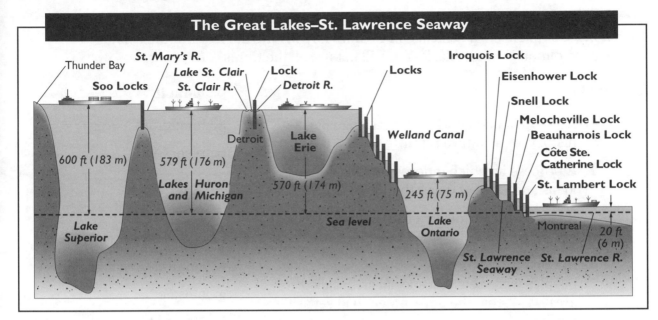

The Great Lakes–St. Lawrence Seaway

17. What does this diagram illustrate?

_____

18. What does the picture tell you about how ships pass through the St. Lawrence Seaway?

_____

19. What do the labels tell you about the St. Lawrence Seaway?

_____

20. Between which two lakes is there the greatest drop in elevation?

_____

21. How does this diagram help you understand the St. Lawrence Seaway?

_____

Tests

TEST A

CHAPTER 3

Cultures of the United States and Canada

A. Key Terms

Directions: Complete each sentence in Column I by writing the letter of the correct term from Column II in the blank. You will not use all the terms. *(10 points)*

Column I

_____ 1. A group of people who share a language, a history, or a culture is a(n) _____ .

_____ 2. A process in which different cultures share ideas and ways of doing things is a(n) _____ .

_____ 3. A place with a wide variety of cultures has _____ .

_____ 4. In Canada and the United States, indigenous peoples were sent to a special area, called a(n) _____ , that the government had set aside for them.

_____ 5. Canada's Inuits call their new territory _____ .

Column II

a. immigrant

b. reserve

c. cultural diversity

d. custom

e. ethnic group

f. cultural exchange

g. mosaic

h. Nunavut

B. Key Concepts

Directions: Write the letter of the correct answer or ending in each blank. *(45 points)*

_____ 6. What is one example of cultural exchange during the settlement of North America?
   a. The Spanish introduced horses to North America.
   b. Native Americans ate a great deal of fish.
   c. European settlers took Native American lands.
   d. Spanish and French explorers came to North America looking for wealth.

_____ 7. How did the contributions of Russian settlers in the Midwest change American life here?
   a. They learned how to trap and hunt forest animals.
   b. They developed a new language.
   c. They invented a kind of work pants.
   d. They introduced a type of wheat that could grow well in the Midwestern climate.

_____ 8. Before the Europeans arrived, the culture of Native Americans living in North America was influenced by
   a. where they lived.
   b. the crops they grew.
   c. the clothes they made.
   d. the types of houses they built.

_____ **9.** In the United States, foods, accents, pastimes, and music
    a. are the same everywhere.
    b. all originated in Russia.
    c. vary from region to region.
    d. are the same as in Canada.

_____ **10.** The two national languages of Canada are
    a. Spanish and English.
    b. French and Spanish.
    c. French and English.
    d. Dutch and English.

_____ **11.** Because many French Canadians of Quebec are worried about preserving their heritage, they want Quebec to become
    a. the capital of the country.
    b. a French colony.
    c. a separate country.
    d. part of the United States.

_____ **12.** How do Canada's native peoples intend to preserve their cultures?
    a. by becoming independent
    b. by moving to reserves
    c. by using their own languages in their schools
    d. by using English on the street signs in their communities

_____ **13.** In order to preserve their cultural identity, Canada's Inuits moved
    a. to Newfoundland.
    b. to their new territory.
    c. to the United States.
    d. to Quebec.

_____ **14.** What country, according to most Canadians, has too much influence on their culture?
    a. Great Britain
    b. France
    c. the United States
    d. Spain

C. Critical Thinking

Directions: Answer the following questions on the back of this paper or on a separate sheet of paper. *(20 points)*

15. Identifying Central Issues Describe one example of cultural exchange in your community involving people from different ethnic groups.

16. Making Comparisons Explain a similarity and a difference in the ways different ethnic groups live in the United States and Canada.

D. Skills

Directions: Complete the concept map to show contributions of people from Spanish and Chinese ethnic groups to cultural diversity. *(25 points)*

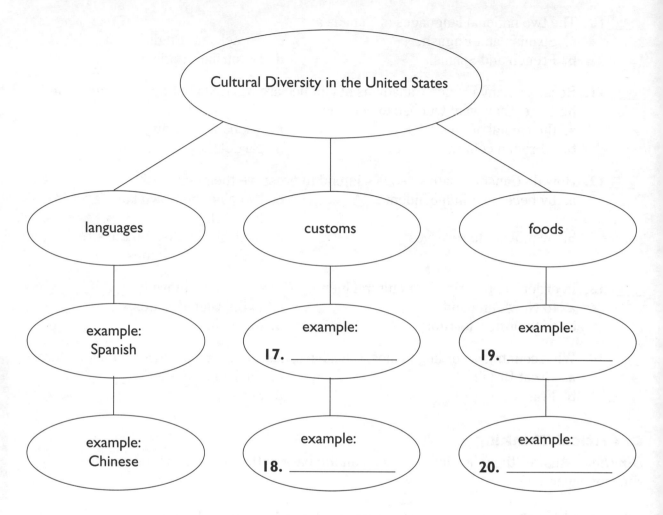

17.–18. Write an example of a custom in each of the ovals 17 and 18.

19.–20. Write an example of a food in each of the ovals 19 and 20.

21. How is it helpful to organize information in a concept map?

_____

_____

_____

Cultures of the United States and Canada

A. Key Terms

Directions: Match the definitions in Column I with the terms in Column II. Write the correct letter in each blank. You will not use all the terms. *(10 points)*

Column I

_____ 1. a process in which different cultures share ideas and ways of doing things

_____ 2. a wide variety of cultures

_____ 3. an area set aside by a government for indigenous peoples

_____ 4. a group of people who share a language, a history, and a culture

_____ 5. the Inuits' new territory

Column II

a. cultural exchange

b. Nunavut

c. immigrant

d. cultural diversity

e. cultural identity

f. ethnic group

g. regional difference

h. reserve

i. Chippewa

B. Key Concepts

Directions: Write the letter of the correct answer or ending in each blank. *(45 points)*

_____ 6. How did Native American groups influence each other's cultures?
   a. by trading with each other
   b. by living in different areas of the country
   c. by growing crops
   d. by hunting animals for food

_____ 7. Native Americans teaching English settlers how to grow local foods is an example of
   a. regional differences.
   b. cultural exchange.
   c. ethnic groups.
   d. cultural similarities.

_____ 8. One way in which immigrants change American life is by
   a. studying American laws.
   b. learning English.
   c. refusing to speak their native languages.
   d. bringing their ethnic customs with them.

Tests

_____ 9. How did Russian settlers change the Midwest?
    a. by bringing iron cooking pots
    c. by creating a popular kind of work pants
    b. by bringing a kind of hardy wheat from their homeland
    d. by developing a new language

_____ 10. Canada's official language(s) is (are)
    a. English and French.
    b. French and Spanish.
    c. English.
    d. French.

_____ 11. Many French Canadians want to preserve their heritage by
    a. adopting the French constitution.
    b. making French the official language of Canada.
    c. making Quebec a separate country.
    d. becoming part of France.

_____ 12. How do Canada's new laws help native peoples to preserve their culture?
    a. by finding them new homes on reserves
    b. by forcing schools to teach French Canadian history
    c. by allowing English in their schools
    d. by allowing them to use their own languages in their schools

_____ 13. In order to regain their cultural identity, Canada's Inuits moved
    a. to Newfoundland.
    b. to their new territory.
    c. to the United States.
    d. to the Arctic.

_____ 14. What country, according to most Canadians, has too much influence on their culture?
    a. Mexico
    b. France
    c. England
    d. the United States

C. Critical Thinking

Directions: Answer the following questions on the back of this paper or on a separate sheet of paper. *(20 points)*

15. **Identifying Central Issues** In what ways is your community like a cultural kaleidoscope? In your answer, identify and briefly discuss two different cultural influences in your community.

16. **Expressing Problems Clearly** What are two ways in which Canada's indigenous peoples are preserving their cultures?

D. Skills

Directions: Complete the concept map to show details about Canada's people.
(25 points)

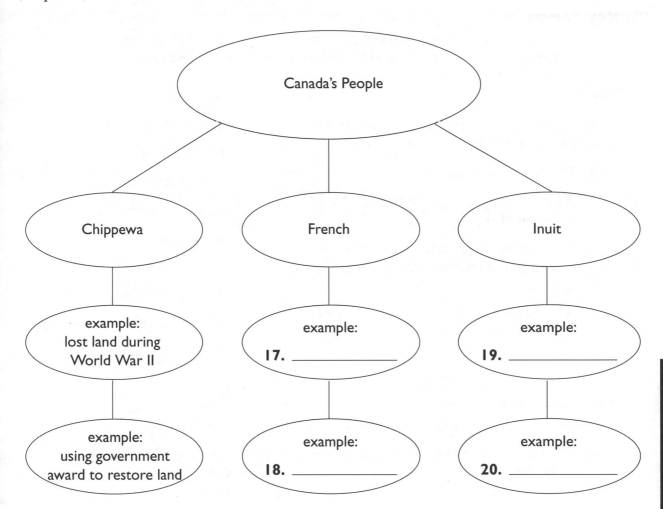

17.–18. Write an example of a detail about Canada's French people in ovals
17 and 18.

19.–20. Write an example of a detail about Canada's Inuit people in ovals
19 and 20.

21. How is it helpful to organize information in a concept map?

_____

_____

Tests

TEST A

CHAPTER 4

Exploring the United States

A. Key Terms

Directions: Complete each sentence in Column I by writing the letter of the correct term from Column II in the blank. You will not use all the terms. *(10 points)*

Column I

_____ **1.** In a(n) _____ , cities and suburbs are so close together that they form one big urban area.

_____ **2.** The South is part of the _____ .

_____ **3.** A farmer grows several different kinds of crops on a(n) _____ .

_____ **4.** To counter the problems caused by freeways and air pollution, San Jose built a(n) _____ system.

_____ **5.** A region's _____ is the average number of people per square mile.

Column II

a. recession

b. mass transit

c. population density

d. industrialization

e. Sun Belt

f. corporate farm

g. megalopolis

h. forty-niner

i. mixed-crop farm

B. Key Concepts

Directions: Write the letter of the best answer in each blank. *(45 points)*

_____ **6.** What is the most densely populated region of the United States?
   a. the South   **c.** the Northeast
   b. the Midwest   **d.** the West

_____ **7.** From the 1890s to the 1940s, most immigrants entering the United States arrived at
   a. cities in the Midwest.   **c.** cities in the West.
   b. Ellis Island   **d.** port cities in the South.

_____ **8.** Features that make much of the South a great place for growing crops include
   a. ports and industry.   **c.** industry and climate.
   b. rich soil and climate. **d.** trade routes.

_____ **9.** Over the past 50 years, the South has changed from an agriculture-based economy to
    a. a trade-based economy.
    b. a mining-based economy.
    c. a forestry-based economy.
    d. an industry-based economy.

_____ **10.** Many farmers have sold or left their lands since 1980 because of
    a. a population decline in the Midwest.
    b. an increase in mixed-crop farms.
    c. an economic recession.
    d. environmental problems.

_____ **11.** What factor contributed to Chicago's rise as a steel-making and manufacturing center in the late 1800s?
    a. Railroads were built.
    b. The population increased.
    c. Corporate farms declined.
    d. Mixed-crop farms increased.

_____ **12.** The natural resources of the West include animals, plants, soil, and
    a. thermal energy.
    b. trade routes.
    c. communication systems.
    d. minerals.

_____ **13.** How did the California Gold Rush affect the region?
    a. Few towns developed.
    b. The population quickly increased.
    c. People quickly returned to the East.
    d. People did not develop the area's natural resources.

_____ **14.** Where is the District of Columbia located?
    a. in Georgia
    b. between the states of North Carolina and South Carolina
    c. between the states of Maryland and Virginia
    d. in the West

C. Critical Thinking

Directions: Answer the following questions on the back of this paper or on a separate sheet of paper. *(20 points)*

15. Making Comparisons Explain the similarities and differences between corporate farms and mixed-crop farms.

16. Drawing Conclusions Identify three problems resulting from urban sprawl in the western region of the United States. If these problems are not solved, what will the outcome likely be?

Tests

D. Skills

Directions: Use the circle graph below to answer the following questions. *(25 points)*

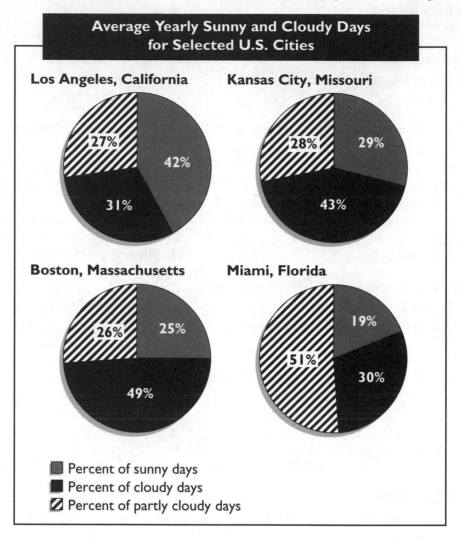

Average Yearly Sunny and Cloudy Days for Selected U.S. Cities

Los Angeles, California
27% 42% 31%

Kansas City, Missouri
28% 29% 43%

Boston, Massachusetts
26% 25% 49%

Miami, Florida
19% 51% 30%

■ Percent of sunny days
■ Percent of cloudy days
▨ Percent of partly cloudy days

17. What U.S. cities are shown on the circle graphs?

_____

18. What information do the circle graphs show?

_____

19. Which city has the most sunny days? Which city has the fewest?

_____

20. Which city has the most cloudy days? Which city has the fewest?

_____

21. Describe the weather in Los Angeles.

_____

Exploring the United States

A. Key Terms

Directions: Match the definitions in Column I with the terms in Column II. Write the correct letter in each blank. You will not use all the terms. *(10 points)*

Column I

_____ **1.** to travel to work each day

_____ **2.** substances like plastics, paint, and asphalt

_____ **3.** the process of changing to an industry-based economy from an agriculture-based economy

_____ **4.** a farm that grows several different kinds of crops

_____ **5.** the first miners of the Gold Rush

Column II

a. petrochemicals

b. urban sprawl

c. industrialization

d. mass transit

e. recession

f. commute

g. forty-niners

h. megalopolis

i. mixed-crop farm

B. Key Concepts

Directions: Write the letter of the best answer in each blank. *(45 points)*

_____ **6.** Today, the economic centers of the Northeast are its
   a. timberlands.
   b. small fishing ports.
   c. farming communities.
   d. cities.

_____ **7.** The most densely populated region of the United States is
   a. the Southeast.
   b. the Northeast.
   c. the West.
   d. the South.

_____ **8.** What is one factor that contributed to the tremendous growth of industry in Philadelphia?
   a. its location near land and water transportation routes
   b. its size
   c. its historical importance during the American Revolution
   d. its reputation as the nation's "money capital"

Tests

_____ 9. As a result of the South's rich soil and climate, its early economy focused on
  a. industry.
  b. trade.
  c. farming.
  d. mining.

_____ 10. Which city hosted the 1996 Summer Olympic Games?
  a. Boston
  b. Atlanta
  c. San Francisco
  d. Miami

_____ 11. For the past few decades, the population of the Sun Belt has been
  a. decreasing.
  b. rising.
  c. staying the same.
  d. moving to the Northeast.

_____ 12. Beginning in the early 1980s, many farmers had to leave or sell their farms because of
  a. an upturn in the economy.
  b. the failure of their crops.
  c. a recession.
  d. poor climate.

_____ 13. What factor contributed to Chicago's development as a steel-making and manufacturing center in the late 1800s?
  a. The economy improved.
  b. Railroads were built.
  c. Farms surrounded the city.
  d. There were different ethnic groups in the city.

_____ 14. Early settlers came to the West because of the region's
  a. location.
  b. natural resources.
  c. industry.
  d. trade routes.

C. Critical Thinking

Directions: Answer the following questions on the back of this paper or on a separate sheet of paper. *(20 points)*

15. **Drawing Conclusions** Why do you think colonists founded the cities of the Northeast along rivers or near the Atlantic Ocean?

16. **Identifying Central Issues** How has industrialization affected the South over the past 50 years?

D. Skills

Directions: Use the circle graph below to answer the following questions. *(25 points)*

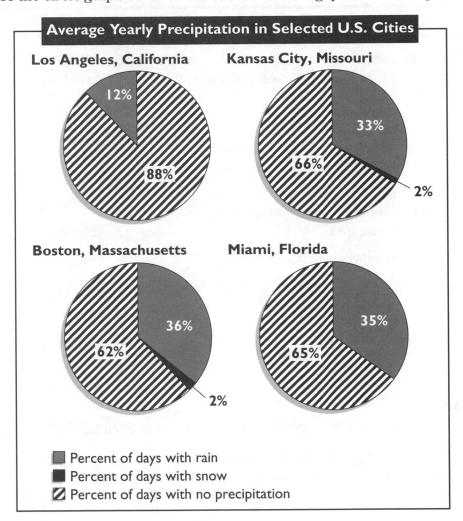

Average Yearly Precipitation in Selected U.S. Cities

Los Angeles, California

12%

88%

Kansas City, Missouri

33%

66%

2%

Boston, Massachusetts

36%

62%

2%

Miami, Florida

35%

65%

☐ Percent of days with rain
■ Percent of days with snow
▨ Percent of days with no precipitation

17. What U.S. cities are shown on the circle graphs?

_____

18. What information is shown on the circle graphs?

_____

19. Which city has the most rainy days? Which city has the fewest?

_____

20. Which cities have the most snowy days?

_____

21. Compare the amount of precipitation in Los Angeles to the amount in the other cities.

_____

Tests

TEST A

CHAPTER
5

Exploring Canada

A. Key Terms

Directions: Complete each sentence in Column I by writing the letter of the correct term from Column II in the blank. You will not use all the terms. *(10 points)*

Column I

_____ **1.** A person living in Quebec who wants the province to break away from Canada is a ____ .

_____ **2.** ____ means "related to navigation or commerce on the sea."

_____ **3.** A natural resistance to a disease is a(n) ____ .

_____ **4.** A giant, carved ____ includes the symbols for a group, a clan, or a family.

_____ **5.** The ____ is a spectacular natural light show that can be seen in the Northern Hemisphere.

Column II

a. maritime

b. boomtown

c. aurora borealis

d. separatist

e. Quiet Revolution

f. totem pole

g. Montreal

h. immunity

i. Pacific Rim

B. Key Concepts

Directions: Write the letter of the correct answer or ending in each blank. *(45 points)*

_____ **6.** Which statement best describes the government of Canada?
    a. The monarch of Britain has total control over Canada.
    b. Canada has complete power over its own government.
    c. The Canadian Parliament is ruled by the United States.
    d. The prime minister is the monarch of Canada.

_____ **7.** What was the result of the 1995 referendum held in Quebec?
    a. Quebec separated from Canada and became independent.
    b. French became the official language of Quebec.
    c. Quebec remained a Canadian province.
    d. Quebec became part of France.

_____ **8.** One way that European settlement changed the lives of the native peoples in the Plains region was by
    a. exposing them to new diseases.
    b. building schools for their children.
    c. giving them free land.
    d. teaching them how to farm their land.

_____ 9. What happened after Canada advertised free land in European newspapers in the late 1800s and early 1900s?
　　　a. Immigration decreased.
　　　b. Immigration increased.
　　　c. People left Canada for Europe.
　　　d. Canadians moved from the farms to the cities.

_____ 10. Early Spanish, British, and Russian explorers of what is now British Columbia came to the region in order to
　　　a. settle.
　　　b. farm.
　　　c. trade.
　　　d. mine.

_____ 11. What was one effect of the gold rush of 1858 on Vancouver Island?
　　　a. Farming increased.
　　　b. Manufacturing decreased.
　　　c. The population increased.
　　　d. Immigration decreased.

_____ 12. How have residents of Canada's eastern coast dealt with changes in the fishing industry?
　　　a. They have completely given up fishing.
　　　b. They only fish for cod.
　　　c. They have banned aquaculture.
　　　d. They have explored other industries such as fish processing.

_____ 13. How has the geography and climate of the Northern Territories influenced life there?
　　　a. Very few people live there.
　　　b. Most of Canada's population lives there.
　　　c. No indigenous peoples live there.
　　　d. Only gold prospectors live there.

_____ 14. How do Canada's territories differ from Canadian provinces?
　　　a. More wheat is grown there.
　　　b. No English is spoken there.
　　　c. They are governed differently.
　　　d. The terrain is less rugged.

C. Critical Thinking

Directions: Answer the following questions on the back of this paper or on a separate sheet of paper. *(20 points)*

15. **Identify Central Issues** Explain how the ways of life of many native peoples in the Plains region of North America ended in the 1870s.

16. **Recognizing Cause and Effect** How did the completion of the Canadian Pacific Railway affect life in Canada?

Tests

D. Skills

Directions: Read the following topic ideas for a one-page paper. Then answer the questions below. Write your answers in the blanks provided. *(25 points)*

- Topic A: Jacques Cartier's discovery in 1535 of what is now Quebec
- Topic B: The immigration of Central and Eastern European people to the Canadian prairies
- Topic C: A gold mine on Vancouver Island

17. Which topic would you choose to write about? Does the topic you chose describe a process, an event, or a thing?

_____

18. Who is your audience?

_____

19. What are two research sources you would use?

_____

20. How would you organize your paper?

_____

21. What would be your next step, before you begin writing your paper?

_____

Exploring Canada

A. Key Terms

Directions: Match the definitions in Column I with the terms in Column II. Write the correct letter in each blank. You will not use all the terms. *(10 points)*

Column I

_____ **1.** a person who speaks French as a first language

_____ **2.** northern lights

_____ **3.** self-governing

_____ **4.** a settlement whose only purpose was to meet the needs of miners

_____ **5.** forced to leave

Column II

a. maritime

b. boomtown

c. separatist

d. exiled

e. immunity

f. aurora borealis

g. autonomous

h. Francophone

B. Key Concepts

Directions: Write the letter of the correct answer or ending in each blank. *(45 points)*

_____ **6.** The largest cultural group living in Quebec today are the descendants of
   a. British settlers.
   b. French colonists.
   c. Spanish explorers.
   d. American loyalists.

_____ **7.** What is the Canadian Shield?
   a. the official symbol of the Canadian government
   b. a fertile plains area in Canada
   c. a rugged land mass in northern Canada
   d. the name of the Canadian southern federation

_____ **8.** Immigrants from Central and Eastern Europe came to the Canadian Plains in the late 1800s and early 1900s in response to an offer of
   a. free transportation to Canada.
   b. an education for their children.
   c. free land in the Prairie Provinces.
   d. jobs in factories.

_____ 9. Why did the ways of life of many indigenous people in the Plains region of North America end in the late 1870s?
   a. European descendants built factories on their lands.
   b. European descendants built schools to educate them.
   c. European descendants began moving from Canada back to their homelands.
   d. European descendants began killing off the buffalo herds.

_____ 10. In 1858, what event significantly changed life on Vancouver Island?
   a. the establishment of Victoria, a small trading village.
   b. the discovery of a trade route to the Pacific Ocean.
   c. the discovery of gold along Fraser River.
   d. the arrival of Russian explorers.

_____ 11. British Columbia's geography and trade partners create a strong link with the area known as
   a. the Pacific Rim.
   b. Western Europe.
   c. Eastern Europe.
   d. South China.

_____ 12. Which natural resources have greatly influenced the economy of the Atlantic Provinces?
   a. gold and silver
   b. coal and natural gas
   c. water and oil
   d. water and wood

_____ 13. How did life in Acadia change in 1763?
   a. People of French descent were exiled.
   b. Britain surrendered its claim to the land.
   c. Indigenous peoples were exiled.
   d. French became the official language.

_____ 14. A large part of Nunavut's population is made up of
   a. the Cree.
   b. the Inuit.
   c. the French.
   d. the British.

C. Critical Thinking

Directions: Answer the following questions on the back of this paper or on a separate sheet of paper. *(20 points)*

15. **Drawing Conclusions** Why do you think the Canadian government is opposed to Quebec's becoming a separate nation? In your answer, briefly explain why some residents of Quebec want to break away from Canada.

16. **Identifying Central Issues** How did the arrival of European settlers in Canada affect the indigenous peoples already living there?

D. Skills

Directions: Read the following topic ideas for a one-page paper. Then answer the questions below. Write your answers in the blanks provided. *(25 points)*

- Topic A: The arrival of James Cook, a British explorer, on Vancouver Island
- Topic B: The building of the Canadian Pacific Railway
- Topic C: The locomotive engine used on trains traveling on the Canadian Pacific Railway

17. Which topic would you choose to write about? Does the topic you chose describe a process, an event, or a thing?

_____

18. Who is your audience?

_____

19. What are two research sources you would use?

_____

20. How would you organize your paper?

_____

21. What would be your next step, before you begin writing your paper?

_____

Tests

FINAL EXAM A

The United States and Canada

A. Key Terms

Directions: Complete each sentence in Column I by writing the letter of the correct term from Column II in the blank. You will not use all the terms. *(10 points)*

Column I

_____ **1.** A huge, slow-moving sheet of ice is a(n) _____ .

_____ **2.** The change from making goods by hand to making them by machine is called the _____ .

_____ **3.** Fish farming, or _____, is a growing industry in the Atlantic Provinces.

_____ **4.** The process of changing from an agriculture-based economy to an industry-based economy is called _____ .

_____ **5.** A natural resistance to disease is a(n) _____ .

Column II

a. glacier

b. immunity

c. separatist

d. Industrial Revolution

e. tributary

f. commute

g. industrialization

h. aquaculture

i. cultural diversity

B. Key Concepts

Directions: Write the letter of the best answer in each blank. *(45 points)*

_____ **6.** The landform that lies between the Rocky and Appalachian mountains is a
    a. low mountain range.   **c.** coastal area.
    b. huge plains area.   **d.** swamp.

_____ **7.** Which statement best describes the climates of the United States and Canada?
    a. Most of the United States is very cold, while Canada has a mild climate.
    c. Much of Canada is very cold, while the United States has a more varied climate.
    b. The United States and Canada have the same climate.
    d. The United States has a warm climate, while the climate of Canada is mild.

_____ **8.** Why did English settlers come to America?
    a. to find wealth
    b. to enslave the Native Americans
    c. to start a new life
    d. to find new trade routes to Asia

_____ 9. After Abraham Lincoln was elected President in 1860, some Southern states
   a. withdrew from the United States.
   b. wanted to abolish slavery.
   c. became colonies of Great Britain.
   d. issued the Emancipation Proclamation.

_____ 10. One way in which the Spanish changed Native American life was by
   a. building schools in North America.
   b. bringing horses to North America.
   c. teaching Native Americans how to farm.
   d. teaching Native Americans about medicinal plants.

_____ 11. After the recession of the 1980s, mixed-crop farms in the American Midwest were replaced by
   a. industries.
   b. mines.
   c. corporate farms.
   d. plantations.

_____ 12. In 2000, ceremonies and festivals were held in Canada to commemorate the 1,000th anniversary of the Vikings' landing at
   a. Ontario.
   c. Newfoundland.
   b. Quebec.
   d. Yukon Territory.

_____ 13. In order to preserve their French culture, many people in Quebec want to
   a. become a colony of France.
   b. get better-paying jobs.
   c. require immigrants to learn English.
   d. separate from Canada.

_____ 14. Why did the ways of life of indigenous people in the Plains region of North America end in the late 1870s?
   a. Many indigenous people left the United States for Europe.
   b. The government encouraged indigenous people to move to the cities.
   c. descendants of Europeans began killing off the buffalo herds.
   d. The population of the indigenous people grew at a tremendous rate.

C. Critical Thinking

Directions: Answer the following questions on the back of this paper or on a separate sheet of paper. *(20 points)*

15. **Making Comparisons**   Explain the similarities and differences between the Civil War in the United States and the Quiet Revolution in Quebec.

16. **Identifying Central Issues**   How did the arrival of European settlers in North America affect the lives and the cultures of the indigenous peoples there? Use two facts from your textbook in your answer.

D. Skills

Directions: Use the population distribution map of Canada below to answer the questions. Write your answers in the blanks provided. *(25 points)*

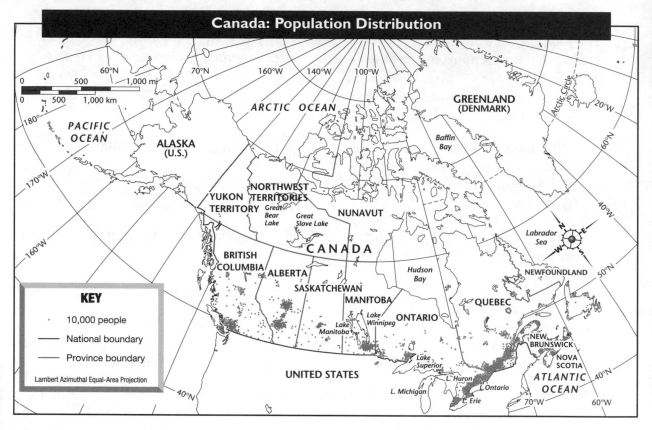

Canada: Population Distribution

KEY

· 10,000 people

— National boundary

— Province boundary

Lambert Azimuthal Equal-Area Projection

17. What country is shown on the map?

_____

18. How is the population represented on the map? How many people does each symbol stand for?

_____

19. Where do the people of Canada live?

_____

20. Where do most of the people of Canada live?

_____

21. Why do you think the population of Canada is distributed the way it is?

_____

The United States and Canada

A. Key Terms

Directions: Match the definitions in Column I with the terms in Column II. Write the correct letter in each blank. You will not use all the terms. *(10 points)*

Column I

_____ **1.** a river that flows into a larger river

_____ **2.** lights caused by the reaction that occurs when winds from the sun hit gases in Earth's atmosphere

_____ **3.** a person who wanted to end slavery

_____ **4.** a group of people who share a language, a history, and a culture

_____ **5.** a region in which cities and suburbs are so close that they form one big urban area

Column II

a. aurora borealis

b. glacier

c. recession

d. tributary

e. megalopolis

f. separatist

g. ethnic group

h. geographic diversity

i. abolitionist

B. Key Concepts

Directions: Write the letter of the correct answer or ending in each blank. *(45 points)*

_____ **6.** What is the largest mountain system in North America?
    a. the Appalachian Mountains
    b. the Rocky Mountains
    c. the Sierra Nevada
    d. the Cascades

_____ **7.** Geographers have identified four major kinds of plant life in the United States and Canada: tundra, grassland, desert scrub, and
    a. tropical.
    b. rain forest.
    c. forest.
    d. plains.

_____ **8.** Spanish and French explorers came to North America looking for
    a. wealth.
    b. settlements.
    c. freedom of religion.
    d. a new life.

Tests

FINAL EXAM   B *(continued)*

_____ 9. How did the idea of Manifest Destiny influence settlement in the United States?
    a. Americans began traveling to the eastern cities to live.
    c. Americans began traveling to the West to settle.
    b. Americans began traveling to Canada to settle.
    d. Americans began traveling to Mexico to live.

_____ 10. The way of life of Native Americans changed after the Spanish introduced
    a. public schools.
    b. medicinal plants.
    c. ways of growing local foods.
    d. horses.

_____ 11. In order to regain their cultural identity, Canada's Inuits moved to
    a. Quebec.
    b. reserves.
    c. the United States.
    d. their new territory.

_____ 12. Which of the following is no longer allowed in the Atlantic Provinces?
    a. cod fishing
    b. fishing
    c. aquaculture
    d. fish processing

_____ 13. British Columbia's geography, ethnic diversity, and trade link the province to
    a. Eastern Europe.
    b. the Pacific Rim.
    c. South America.
    d. Russia.

_____ 14. The two official languages of Canada are
    a. English and Spanish.
    b. French and Spanish.
    c. English and French.
    d. French and German.

C. Critical Thinking

Directions: Answer the following questions on the back of this paper or on a separate sheet of paper. *(20 points)*

15. **Drawing Conclusions**   Canada has more land than the United States, but the United States has 10 times more people than Canada. Why do you think this is so?

16. **Making Comparisons**   Explain the similarities and differences in the ways the United States and Canada each achieved independence.

D. Skills

Directions: Read the following topic ideas for a one-page paper. Then answer the questions below. Write your answers in the blanks provided. *(25 points)*

- Topic A: The arrival of European explorers and settlers in North America
- Topic B: The start of the Civil War
- Topic C: A plantation in the pre–Civil War South

17. Which topic would you choose to write about? Does the topic you chose describe a process, an event, or a thing?

_____

18. Who is your audience?

_____

19. What are two research sources you would use?

_____

20. How would you organize your paper?

_____

21. What would be your next step, before you begin writing your paper?

_____

Tests

Answer Key

Chapter 1

Test A

1. d	**2.** a	**3.** i	**4.** g	**5.** e
6. b	**7.** c	**8.** a	**9.** d	**10.** c
11. d	**12.** b	**13.** b	**14.** b	

15. Answers may vary, but should include reference to the following: Canada's geography and climate make vast areas of the country difficult for people to live in. The Canadian Shield, a huge region of ancient rock, is very rugged. As a result, more than half of the country's population lives in the smallest land region, the St. Lawrence Lowlands. Also, the very cold climate in much of the country limits population growth.

16. Answers may vary, but should include the following: A farmer in the United States would have settled in an area with rich soil, a mild climate, and access to rivers or other bodies of water. Possible areas include: the eastern and southern coastal plains or the Great Plains. In Canada, a farmer would probably have settled in the St. Lawrence Lowlands, where the soil is fertile and there is access to water routes for trade and shipping.

17. The title identifies the map as a population distribution map of western Canada.

18. Population is represented by dots.

19. Each dot stands for 10,000 people.

20. The southern half of this area has the highest population density.

21. The more northern part of the region is much colder and has less rainfall. Also, it is largely covered with forests or tundra.

Test B

1. c	**2.** a	**3.** i	**4.** f	**5.** b
6. c	**7.** a	**8.** b	**9.** c	**10.** c
11. c	**12.** b	**13.** d	**14.** a	

15. Answers may vary, but should include the following: The two waterways are the St. Lawrence River and the Great Lakes. Since these waterways are important transportation and manufacturing centers for both countries,

the United States and Canada are likely trade partners.

16. Answers may vary, but should include the following: The Rocky Mountains extend north to south along the western section of the continent; in the East, the Appalachian Mountains stretch about 1,500 miles. The Appalachians meet the Laurentian Highlands in Canada. Between these two mountain systems lies a huge plains area, called the Great Plains and the Central Plains in the United States and the Interior Plains in Canada.

17. The title identifies the map as a population distribution map of central and eastern Canada.

18. Population is represented by dots.

19. Each symbol, or dot, stands for 10,000 people.

20. Most people live in the southeastern areas of the country, along the border with the United States.

21. The northern area has the lowest population density.

Chapter 2

Test A

1. d	**2.** i	**3.** h	**4.** a	**5.** b
6. b	**7.** a	**8.** c	**9.** d	**10.** b
11. b	**12.** b	**13.** c	**14.** a	

15. Answers may vary, but should include reference to the following: The American Revolution was an armed conflict between Great Britain and the American colonies. At the end of the war, the colonies won their independence from Great Britain, and the United States of America was established as a separate country. Canada's peaceful revolution did not involve violence. Instead, after the British Parliament accepted the British North American Act, Canada became a dominion. It was still subject to Great Britain, but a central Canadian government would run the country.

16. Answers may vary, but should include reference to the following: The United States and Canada worked together to solve the problem

Answer Key

of moving ships from one water level to another by building the St. Lawrence Seaway. It is a system of locks, canals, and dams that allows water transportation from the Great Lakes all the way to the Atlantic Ocean. The St. Lawrence Seaway, completed in 1959, makes it easier for both countries to trade with each other and with Europe.

17. The diagram shows how a locomotive works.

18. The pictures illustrate how the steam travels through the engine and makes the wheels turn.

19. The labels identify the main parts of a locomotive and how they work. Movement is shown by arrows and labels.

20. any three: boiler, firebox, steam pipe, superheater pipes, steam chest, cylinder, pistons, drive rods

21. Answers may vary, but students should note that while the pictures illustrate the different parts of a locomotive, the labels explain what the parts are and how they work together.

Test B

1. c	2. a	3. g	4. e	5. h
6. c	7. c	8. a	9. d	10. b
11. c	12. d	13. d	14. b	

15. Answers may vary, but should include reference to one of the following issues: protecting the whales from extinction; water pollution of the Cuyahoga River; acid rain; or renewing forests.

16. Answers may vary, but should include reference to the following: The Spanish settlers spread out across the United States and often enslaved Native Americans. Spanish missionaries tried to make Native Americans more like Europeans. French explorers, however, claimed land along the St. Lawrence and Mississippi rivers. French traders and missionaries often lived among the Native Americans and learned their languages. Unlike the Spanish, they did not take over Native American land.

17. the Great Lakes and St. Lawrence Seaway

18. Ships move from higher water levels to lower ones through a series of locks over several bodies of water.

19. They tell you the names of the lakes, rivers, locks, and canals that make up the St. Lawrence Seaway. They also tell the water level of each lake.

20. Lake Erie and Lake Ontario

21. Answers may vary, but students may note that the labels and illustration help them understand how ships can move from one water level to another between the Great Lakes and on the St. Lawrence Seaway.

Chapter 3

Test A

1. e	2. f	3. c	4. b	5. h
6. a	7. d	8. a	9. c	10. c
11. c	12. c	13. b	14. c	

15. Answers may vary, but might include an ethnic restaurant that also includes more traditional American food on its menu.

16. Answers may vary, but might include reference to the following: Similarity: Immigrants came to both countries in search of better lives. Difference: In the United States, members of different ethnic groups may disagree, but they do not talk about forming separate states. However, many French Canadians of Quebec want to form a separate country.

17–18. Answers may vary, but could include music and dragon parades.

19–20. Answers may vary, but could include tacos and stir fry.

21. Answers may vary. Possible answer: It sometimes helps to see information mapped out rather than reading it in a paragraph. It works like an outline.

Test B

1. a	2. d	3. h	4. f	5. b
6. a	7. b	8. d	9. b	10. a
11. c	12. d	13. b	14. d	

Answer Key

15. Answers may vary, but should include references to two cultural influences, such as ethnic music and ethnic restaurants.

16. Answers may vary, but could include reference to new laws that allow indigenous peoples to use their own languages in their schools. Also, the Inuits, who were fearful of losing their cultural identity, have secured a new territory, Nunavut.

17–18. Answers may vary, but could include the fact that Quebec residents speak French, many street signs are in French, and certain laws promote French culture and heritage.

19–20. Answers may vary, but could include the fact that Inuits used to live in the Arctic and have now moved into their new territory, Nunavut.

21. It sometimes helps to see information mapped out rather than reading it in a paragraph. It works like an outline.

Chapter 4

Test A

1. g   2. e   3. i   4. b   5. c
6. c   7. b   8. b   9. d   10. c
11. a   12. d   13. b   14. c

15. Answers may vary, but should include reference to the following: Mixed-crop farms are operated by families. These farms grow several different kinds of crops. However, corporate farms are large farms that are operated by agricultural companies. Corporate farmers use machines and computers to do much of the farmwork and employ fewer workers than the mixed-crop farms.

16. Answers may vary, but should include reference to the following: Three problems include air pollution, traffic congestion, and water pollution from industrial waste. If these problems are not corrected through mass transit systems and anti-pollution legislation, the quality of life in these cities will deteriorate.

17. Los Angeles; Boston; Kansas City; and Miami

18. percentage of sunny, cloudy, and partly cloudy days each year for Los Angeles, Boston, Kansas City, and Miami

19. Los Angeles; Miami

20. Boston; Miami

21. Students may conclude that the weather in Los Angeles is sunnier than in most other areas of the country; Los Angeles has the greatest number of sunny days and the second lowest number of cloudy and partly cloudy days.

Test B

1. f   2. a   3. c   4. i   5. g
6. d   7. b   8. a   9. c   10. b
11. b   12. c   13. b   14. b

15. Answers may vary, but should include reference to the importance of water transportation for the early colonists. Water routes enabled them to travel and transport goods from one colony to another; being near the Atlantic Ocean gave the colonial cities access to boats from England and other European countries.

16. Answers may vary, but should include reference to the following: Most people in the South today live in cities; more people work in industry-related jobs than in agriculture-based jobs; textiles, technology, transportation, and tourism are all important to the South's economy today.

17. Los Angeles; Boston; Kansas City; and Miami

18. percentage of days each year with and without precipitation for Los Angeles, Boston, Kansas City, and Miami

19. Boston; Los Angeles

20. Boston and Kansas City

21. Los Angeles has the least precipitation of the cities shown.

Chapter 5

Test A

1. d   2. a   3. h   4. f   5. c
6. b   7. c   8. a   9. b   10. c
11. c   12. d   13. a   14. c

Answer Key

15. Answers may vary, but should include reference to the following: Descendants of Europeans killed off the buffalo herds that were central to the lives of indigenous peoples. At the same time, the governments of Canada and the United States took over the indigenous peoples' land and sent them to live on reserves.

16. Answers will vary, but should include reference to the following: The railroad provided a way of uniting Canada from Montreal to Vancouver. Building the project attracted immigrants from all over the world. Towns grew up along the railroad, and more people came to Canada.

17. Answers will vary. Topic A describes an event; Topic B describes a process; Topic C describes a thing.

18. teachers and classmates

19. Answers will vary, but students can refer to the Internet, nonfiction books, encyclopedia articles, newspapers of the period, and magazine articles.

20. Topic A—chronological order; Topic B—the steps in the process; Topic C—its purpose and parts

21. writing an outline

Test B

1. h	2. f	3. g	4. b	5. d
6. b	7. c	8. c	9. d	10. c
11. a	12. d	13. a	14. b	

15. Answers may vary, but should include reference to the following: Many people in Quebec who are of French descent are worried that their culture and language might die if Quebec remains part of Canada, and for that reason, many residents of the province demand independence for Quebec. Although the Canadian government did make some changes, such as making French the official language of Quebec, the separatists have declared that they will continue their struggle. If Quebec does separate, it would weaken Canada politically and economically. It might encourage other Canadian provinces to become separate nations as well.

16. Answers will vary, but should include reference to the following: The European settlers destroyed the buffalo herds that were essential to the lives of the indigenous peoples. Also, the arrivals of European immigrants to Canada introduced diseases to which the indigenous people had no immunity. Then the governments of Canada took the land that belonged to the indigenous peoples and forced them to live on reserves.

17. Answers will vary. Topic A describes an event; Topic B describes a process; Topic C describes a thing.

18. teachers and classmates

19. Answers will vary, but students can refer to the Internet, nonfiction books, encyclopedia articles, newspapers of the period, and magazine articles.

20. Topic A—chronological order; Topic B—the steps in the process; Topic C—its purpose and parts

21. writing an outline

Final Exam

Test A

1. a	2. d	3. h	4. g	5. b
6. b	7. c	8. c	9. a	10. b
11. c	12. c	13. d	14. c	

15. Answers will vary, but should include reference to the following: The Civil War was an armed struggle between the Union and the Confederacy that started when some Southern states seceded from the United States. The states left the Union because they thought that President Lincoln would abolish slavery, a system that was central to the Southern economy. However, the Quiet Revolution was a peaceful change in government in which the political party that supported Quebec's separation from Canada won control of the provincial legislature. The new government made French the official language of Quebec. However, Quebec still remained a province of Canada.

Answer Key

16. Answers may vary, but should include reference to the following: Descendants of Europeans changed the culture of the indigenous peoples by taking their land and forcing them to live on reserves, by destroying the buffalo herds that they depended upon, and by introducing diseases to which they had no immunity.

17. Canada

18. by dots; 10,000

19. throughout the country, with the exception of the extreme north

20. along the southern border

21. The climate is milder in the south.

Test B

1. d   2. a   3. i   4. g   5. e

6. b   7. c   8. a   9. c   10. d

11. d   12. a   13. b   14. c

15. Answers may vary, but should include reference to Canada's cold climate, which makes it difficult for people to live in much of the country, and the more varied and generally milder climate of the United States. Also, the Canadian Shield covers about half of Canada. Because the land on the Canadian Shield is so rugged, few people live there.

16. Answers may vary, but should include reference to the following: The American colonies fought the Revolutionary War against Great Britain to gain their independence. Canada also wanted to be independent of British rule. However, it happened gradually, beginning with the British North American Act of 1867, which made Canada a dominion, or self-governing area. At that time, Canada was still subject to Great Britain. However, in 1982, the Canadians wrote a new constitution. It enabled Canadians to change their constitution without Great Britain's permission. At that point, Canada was completely independent.

17. Answers will vary. Topic A describes an event; Topic B describes a process; Topic C describes a thing.

18. teachers and classmates

19. Answers will vary; however, students can refer to nonfiction books, encyclopedia articles, newspapers of the period, and magazine articles.

20. Topic A—chronological order or steps in the process; Topic B—the steps in the process or chronological order; Topic C—its purpose and parts

21. writing an outline

Spanish Support

CARTA PARA LA FAMILIA

LOS ESTADOS UNIDOS Y EL CANADÁ
Geografía física

La Línea Abierta de Ciencias Sociales

Querida familia:

Durante las próximas semanas, en nuestra clase de ciencias sociales estudiaremos a los Estados Unidos y al Canadá. Vamos a observar la geografía, la historia y las culturas de estas dos naciones. A medida que avancemos en el texto, espero que usted pueda compartir con su hijo o hija experiencias personales o información sobre los distintos temas que exploremos.

En el Capítulo 1, vamos a estudiar la tierra, el agua, el clima, la vegetación y los recursos naturales de los Estados Unidos y el Canadá. Mientras su hijo o hija estudia los mapas de este capítulo, puede animarlo o animarla a identificar las regiones y sus climas, la vegetación, los recursos naturales y los accidentes geográficos más sobresalientes.

Hágale preguntas como estas a su hijo o hija: ¿Hay grandes ríos o extensiones de agua cerca de donde vivimos? ¿Cómo es nuestro clima? ¿A qué altura vivimos? ¿A qué latitud? ¿Cómo es nuestra ubicación comparada con otros lugares como Edmonton, Alberta; Phoenix, Arizona; o Honolulú, Hawai? Paseos por las zonas que rodean a su comunidad también pueden ser buenas oportunidades para conversar con su hijo o hija acerca de la geografía de la región.

También podría ver los noticieros o escuchar las noticias con su hijo o hija, prestando especial atención a informes que tengan que ver con el medio ambiente y los recursos naturales. Ayude su hijo o hija a buscar artículos de periódicos o revistas acerca de debates interesantes sobre el uso de recursos naturales tales como los árboles, los minerales y el agua.

En las próximas semanas, es posible que usted reciba más cartas con noticias sobre nuestro estudio de los Estados Unidos y el Canadá. Mientras tanto, espero que tanto usted como su hijo o hija disfruten al trabajar juntos para aprender más sobre la geografía física de los Estados Unidos y el Canadá.

Atentamente,

Nombre _____ Clase _____ Fecha _____

CAPÍTULO 1
**LOS ESTADOS
UNIDOS Y EL CANADÁ**
Geografía física

La tierra y el agua

A. Durante la lectura

Instrucciones: A medida que vayas leyendo la Sección 1, escribe tus respuestas a las siguientes preguntas en los espacios en blanco.

1. ¿En qué continente están los Estados Unidos y el Canadá ubicados?

   _____

2. ¿Qué país tiene más terreno, los Estados Unidos o el Canadá? ¿Cuál tiene más habitantes?

   _____

3. ¿Cuáles son los dos sistemas montañosos más grandes de América del Norte? ¿Qué hay en medio de ellos?

   _____

4. ¿Cuál es el nombre de las dos cordilleras ubicadas en el oeste de los Estados Unidos?

   _____

5. ¿Dónde está ubicado el escudo canadiense? ¿Por qué viven pocas personas allí?

   _____

6. ¿En qué zona vive más de la mitad de la población del Canadá? ¿Cuál es la razón?

   _____

7. ¿Cómo se formaron los Grandes Lagos? ¿Cuándo ocurrió eso?

   _____

8. ¿Cuáles son los dos ríos principales del Canadá?

   _____

9. ¿Por qué es el Río San Lorenzo tan importante?

   _____

B. Repaso de los términos clave

Instrucciones: Para completar cada oración, escribe el término correspondiente en el espacio en blanco.

10. El Río Misuri es un _____ del Misisipí, porque es más pequeño y desemboca en éste.

11. Los Grandes Lagos fueron formados por _____ durante el período glaciar.

12. La _____ está formada por las Montañas Rocosas y divide a los ríos que fluyen hacia el este y el oeste de América del Norte.

Spanish Support

La tierra y el agua

A. Términos y conceptos clave

Instrucciones: Empareja las definiciones de la Columna I con los términos de la Columna II. Escribe la letra correspondiente en cada espacio en blanco.

Columna I

_____ 1. gran masa de hielo que se mueve lentamente

_____ 2. división que separa los ríos que fluyen hacia lados opuestos de un continente

_____ 3. río que desemboca en un río principal

_____ 4. cadena montañosa de los Estados Unidos que al llegar al Canadá se encuentra con las montañas del San Lorenzo

_____ 5. el lugar más caluroso de América del Norte

Columna II

a. divisoria continental

b. los Apalaches

c. el Valle de la Muerte

d. tributario

e. glaciar

B. Ideas principales

Instrucciones: En cada espacio en blanco, escribe la letra que mejor conteste la pregunta.

_____ 6. Los Grandes Lagos fueron formados por
   a. el Río Misisipí.
   b. las Montañas Rocosas.
   c. glaciares.
   d. la Gran Cuenca.

_____ 7. ¿Qué hay entre las Montañas Rocosas y los Apalaches?
   a. una gran llanura
   b. las Cascadas
   c. el Río San Lorenzo
   d. el Valle de la Muerte

_____ 8. ¿Qué accidente geográfico canadiense cubre cerca de la mitad del continente?
   a. las llanuras interiores
   b. el escudo canadiense
   c. la meseta de San Lorenzo
   d. el territorio Yukón

_____ 9. ¿Qué oración describe mejor a los Grandes Lagos?
   a. Son el conjunto de lagos más pequeños del mundo.
   b. Son el conjunto de lagos de agua dulce más grande del mundo.
   c. Son corrientes importantes que desembocan en el Océano Pacífico.
   d. Forman la frontera entre los Estados Unidos y el territorio Yukón.

_____ 10. El Río San Lorenzo es importante porque conecta a
   a. los Grandes Lagos con el Río Misisipí.
   b. los dos ríos principales del Canadá.
   c. las Montañas Rocosas con los Apalaches.
   d. los Grandes Lagos con el Océano Atlántico.

CAPÍTULO 1
LOS ESTADOS UNIDOS Y EL CANADÁ
Geografía física

El clima y la vegetación

A. Durante la lectura

Instrucciones: A medida que vayas leyendo la Sección 2, completa la tabla a continuación con información del clima y la vegetación de los Estados Unidos y el Canadá.

El clima y la vegetación de Los Estados Unidos y el Canadá

Los climas del Canadá	1.
Los climas de los Estados Unidos	2.
Zona de vegetación: La tundra	3.
Zona de vegetación: Las praderas	4.
Zona de vegetación: Los desiertos de matorrales	5.
Zona de vegetación: Los bosques	6.

B. Repaso de los términos clave

Instrucciones: Para completar cada oración, escribe el término correspondiente en el espacio en blanco.

7. región en el lado protegido de una montaña que recibe muy poca lluvia

_____

8. capa de tierra permanentemente congelada

_____

9. región de terrenos planos cubiertos de pastos altos

_____

10. división política territorial en el Canadá, similar a un estado de los Estados Unidos

_____

Spanish Support

EXAMEN DE LA SECCIÓN

El clima y la vegetación

A. Términos y conceptos clave

Instrucciones: Lee las oraciones a continuación. Si una oración es verdadera, escribe V en el espacio en blanco. Si es falsa, escribe F. En otra hoja de papel, vuelve a escribir las oraciones falsas para convertirlas en verdaderas.

_____ **1.** La sombra de lluvia es una región húmeda en el lado protegido de una montaña que recibe mucha lluvia.

_____ **2.** Los trópicos son zonas que quedan entre las líneas de latitud $23\frac{1}{2}°$N y $23\frac{1}{2}°$S.

_____ **3.** La tundra es una región seca y fría que está cubierta de nieve durante seis semanas al año.

_____ **4.** Permafrost es una capa de tierra permanentemente congelada.

_____ **5.** Una provincia es una división geográfica del Canadá.

B. Ideas principales

Instrucciones: En cada espacio en blanco, escribe la letra que mejor conteste la pregunta.

_____ **6.** Los factores que influyen en la variedad de climas de los Estados Unidos y el Canadá incluyen la latitud, las montañas, los océanos y
   a. el tamaño de la región.
   b. la distancia a la Gran Llanura.
   c. la profundidad de los ríos.
   d. la distancia al Ártico.

_____ **7.** Gran parte del clima en el Canadá es
   a. muy frío.
   b. moderado.
   c. fresco.
   d. extremadamente húmedo.

_____ **8.** Un factor importante en el crecimiento de la vegetación tanto en los Estados Unidos como en el Canadá es
   a. los ríos.
   b. el tamaño de la región.
   c. el clima.
   d. la altura de las montañas.

_____ **9.** Los cuatro tipos principales de vegetación natural en los Estados Unidos y el Canadá son: la tundra, las llanuras, los desiertos de matorrales y
   a. el permafrost.
   b. los bosques.
   c. los pantanos.
   d. las llanuras costeras.

_____ **10.** La pradura más extensa del mundo queda en
   a. las zonas costeras de los Estados Unidos.
   b. el territorio Yukón.
   c. las llanuras de América del Norte.
   d. la Gran Bretaña.

CAPÍTULO 1
LOS ESTADOS
UNIDOS Y EL CANADÁ
Geografía física

Los recursos naturales

A. Durante la lectura

Instrucciones: A medida que vayas leyendo la Sección 3, completa las siguientes oraciones.

1. Los Estados Unidos tienen vastas extensiones de _____ .

2. Hasta el siglo XX, la mayoría de las granjas americanas pertenecían a _____ .

3. Cuatro usos importantes del agua en los Estados Unidos son _____ ,

   _____ , _____ , y _____ .

4. Estados Unidos es el segundo productor más grande del mundo de _____ ,

   _____ , y _____ .

5. Cerca del 9 por ciento de la tierra del Canadá es apta para _____ .

6. El escudo canadiense tiene la mayor parte de la _____ de ese país.

7. En las _____ hay grandes depósitos de petróleo y gas natural.

8. Canadá es líder mundial en la producción de _____ .

B. Repaso de los términos clave

Instrucciones: En los espacios en blanco a continuación, escribe las definiciones para los siguientes términos clave.

9. aluvial

   _____

10. hidroelectricidad

   _____

11. empresa agrícola

   _____

Spanish Support

EXAMEN DE LA SECCIÓN

Los recursos naturales

A. Términos y conceptos clave

Instrucciones: Empareja las definiciones de la Columna I con los términos de la Columna II.
Escribe la letra correspondiente en cada espacio en blanco.

Columna I

_____ **I.** Tierra rica depositada por los ríos se conoce como
_____ .

_____ **2.** La represa de ____ produce más hidroelectricidad
que cualquier otra represa de los Estados Unidos.

_____ **3.** Una compañía que administra una granja enorme
es una ____ .

_____ **4.** El oleoducto de Alaska lleva el petróleo crudo hasta
____ .

_____ **5.** Hay extensos terrenos de hortalizas y legumbres en
____ de California.

Columna II

a. el puerto de Valdez

b. aluvial

c. el Valle Imperial

d. empresa agrícola

e. Grand Coulee

B. Ideas principales

Instrucciones: En cada espacio en blanco, escribe la letra que mejor conteste la pregunta.

_____ **6.** ¿Por qué son importantes los ríos San Lorenzo, Misisipí y Misuri?
   a. porque unen el este con el oeste de los Estados Unidos
   b. porque son rutas marítimas importantes
   c. porque crean las fronteras entre los Estados Unidos y el Canadá
   d. porque son los ríos más grandes del mundo

_____ **7.** Hasta el siglo XX, la mayoría de las granjas en los Estados Unidos eran propiedad de
   a. empresas grandes.   **c.** pueblos.
   b. familias.   **d.** corporaciones.

_____ **8.** Las reservas de petróleo más grandes de América del Norte se hallan
   a. a lo largo de la costa este.   **c.** a lo largo de la costa norte de Alaska.
   b. cerca del Río San Lorenzo.   **d.** cerca de los Grandes Lagos.

_____ **9.** ¿Por qué la minería es importante para la economía de los Estados Unidos?
   a. porque emplea a muchos trabajadores
   b. porque representa una gran parte de la economía del país
   c. porque los minerales son transportados al Canadá
   d. porque los minerales son usados en otras industrias

_____ **10.** Las provincias de las llanuras y las tierras bajas del Río San Lorenzo son las principales regiones
   a. agrícolas del Canadá.   **c.** mineras del Canadá.
   b. forestales del Canadá.   **d.** industriales del Canadá.

Nombre _____ Clase _____ Fecha _____

LOS ESTADOS UNIDOS Y EL CANADÁ
Geografía física

CAPÍTULO
1

Pregunta guía:

* ¿Cómo ha afectado la geografía física a las culturas de los Estados Unidos y el Canadá?

<u>Los Estados Unidos y el Canadá son los países ubicados más al norte de América del Norte.</u> Estos dos países son en realidad una sola extensión de tierra. La única división entre ellos son los Grandes Lagos y el Río San Lorenzo. Las cadenas montañosas y las llanuras cruzan por ambos países. Las dos cadenas montañosas más grandes son las Montañas Rocosas en el oeste y los Apalaches en el este. Hay extensas zonas de llanuras planas entre esas dos grandes cadenas montañosas. Al este de los Apalaches hay una llanura que va a lo largo de la costa. Aunque ambos países comparten las mismas características físicas, los Estados Unidos y el Canadá tienen distintos accidentes geográficos.

<u>Las principales extensiones de agua de los Estados Unidos y el Canadá son los cinco Grandes Lagos.</u> Cuatro de ellos están ubicados en ambos países. El río más grande del Canadá es el Río Mackenzie en el oeste y el Río San Lorenzo en el este. El Misisipí, con sus tributarios principales, el Misuri y el Ohio, forma el sistema de ríos más grande de los Estados Unidos.

<u>Debido a que el Canadá está tan al norte, tiene por lo general un clima frío.</u> En el lejano oeste, el Océano Pacífico crea un clima marino moderado. Sin embargo, las zonas en el interior son bastante frías en invierno y muy cálidas en verano. <u>Los Estados Unidos tiene una mayor variedad de climas que el Canadá.</u> Las regiones que están ubicadas más al sur como la Florida y Hawai están en el trópico. La costa oeste de los Estados Unidos, como la del Canadá tiene un clima marino moderado. Al este de la cadena montañosa occidental, la sombra de lluvia es responsable por los vastos desiertos y las regiones áridas. El este de los Estados Unidos tiene diferentes tipos de clima continental que varían de acuerdo con la latitud.

<u>Hay cuatro tipos principales de vegetación en los Estados Unidos y el Canadá.</u> Ellos son: la tundra, que se halla en las lejanas regiones del norte; las llanuras; los desiertos de matorrales y los bosques. Las llanuras se hallan con frecuencia en las planicies de ambos países. Los desiertos de matorrales crecen en las regiones áridas de los Estados Unidos. Los bosques cubren cerca de un tercio de los Estados Unidos y cerca de la mitad del Canadá. Los Estados Unidos tiene grandes extensiones de tierra fértil. En cambio sólo el 9 por ciento de la tierra del Canadá es cultivable. Ambos países tienen agua, minerales, bosques y recursos energéticos en abundancia.

Nombre _____ Clase _____ Fecha _____

CAPÍTULO 1

LOS ESTADOS UNIDOS Y EL CANADÁ
Geografía física

Instrucciones: Lee las oraciones a continuación. Las palabras en negrilla hacen falsa cada oración. Vuelve a escribir cada oración para que sea verdadera. Si necesitas ayuda, usa tu libro texto. Los términos clave de tu libro texto están subrayados. Si es necesario, mira los términos equivalentes en inglés en el glosario de tu libro de texto.

1. Cuando los antiguos <u>glaciares</u> se descongelaron, **crearon depresiones profundas en la tierra.**

_____

2. Un <u>tributario</u> es un **río o corriente que desemboca en un río más pequeño.**

_____

3. La frontera montañosa que evita que **los animales migren de un lado al otro de un continente** se llama la <u>divisoria continental</u>.

_____

4. La <u>sombra de lluvia</u> es una zona en el lado de una montaña **donde rara vez llega el sol.**

_____

5. La zona entre las **líneas de longitud $23\frac{1}{2}°$N y $23\frac{1}{2}°$S** se llama los <u>trópicos</u>.

_____

6. La <u>tundra</u> en el extremo norte del Canadá es **un excelente lugar para el cultivo.**

_____

7. Durante el verano, la superficie del <u>permafrost</u> **permanece congelada.**

_____

8. Hallarás <u>llanuras</u> en las zonas que tienen **clima árido.**

_____

9. Una <u>provincia</u> canadiense es **similar a una ciudad de los Estados Unidos.**

_____

10. La tierra fértil del <u>aluvial</u> es depositada por **los glaciares.**

_____

11. Las <u>empresas agrícolas</u> son **enormes granjas administradas por familias.**

_____

12. La <u>hidroelectricidad</u> puede ser generada por **puentes construidos sobre ríos.**

_____

LOS ESTADOS UNIDOS Y EL CANADÁ
Forjados por su historia

La Línea Abierta de Ciencias Sociales

Querida familia:

Durante los próximos días, vamos a estudiar la historia de los Estados Unidos y el Canadá. Para empezar, vamos a aprender sobre los primeros habitantes de América del Norte y veremos cómo afectó sus vidas la llegada de los europeos. Más adelante, veremos cómo cada país logró su independencia y creció hasta convertirse en una gran potencia industrial.

Su hijo o hija completará un proyecto especial para ampliar su conocimiento de los Estados Unidos y el Canadá. Algunos de los proyectos en que podría participar incluyen: escribir un libro para niños menores, crear un cronograma de la historia de su comunidad, preparar una estación meteorológica para medir y registrar las condiciones del clima en su comunidad y hacer un diorama de los Estados Unidos y el Canadá o de una región más pequeña de uno de esos países. Para ayudar a su hijo o hija con estos proyectos, usted puede, por ejemplo, compartir historias personales e información sobre su comunidad, o puede ayudarle a recopilar información sobre las condiciones del clima en otras partes del país.

Puesto que en este capítulo hay tanta información, le recomiendo enfocarse en un período o evento particular con su hijo o hija, para ayudarle a entenderlo mejor. Quizás puedan leer juntos una novela histórica o visitar lugares de interés histórico en su comunidad y conversar acerca de su importancia.

Espero que tanto usted como su hijo o hija disfruten el estudio de la historia de los Estados Unidos y el Canadá.

Atentamente,

Spanish Support

LECTURA DIRIGIDA Y REPASO

Los primeros americanos y la llegada de los europeos

A. Durante la lectura

Instrucciones: A medida que vayas leyendo la Sección 1, completa la siguiente tabla con la información de los primeros americanos y la llegada de los europeos.

Datos sobre los primeros americanos y la llegada de los europeos

Los primeros americanos	1.
La llegada de los europeos	2.
Los colonizadores ingleses	3.
La separación de la Gran Bretaña	4.

B. Repaso de los términos clave

Instrucciones: Escribe el término clave correspondiente para cada una de las siguientes definiciones.

5. originarios de un lugar en particular

_____

6. personas religiosas que trataban de convertir a otros a su religión

_____

7. persona que debe trabajar por algunos años para obtener su libertad

_____

8. hacienda grande del sur de los Estados Unidos donde por lo general se cultivaba un solo producto

_____

9. rehusar a comprar o a usar ciertos productos o servicios

_____

10. la guerra entre las colonias americanas y la Gran Bretaña

_____

CAPÍTULO 2
LOS ESTADOS UNIDOS Y EL CANADÁ
Forjados por su historia

Los primeros americanos y la llegada de los europeos

A. Términos y conceptos clave

Instrucciones: Empareja las definiciones de la Columna I con los términos de la Columna II. Escribe la letra correspondiente en cada espacio en blanco.

Columna I

_____ **1.** Las personas originarias de un lugar son _____ .

_____ **2.** Las personas que tratan de convertir a otros a su religión son _____ .

_____ **3.** Algunos colonos ingleses llegaron como _____ y trabajaron por años para obtener su libertad.

_____ **4.** Los colonizadores americanos decidieron hacer _____ , es decir, se rehusaron a comprar ciertos productos fabricados en la Gran Bretaña.

_____ **5.** Una hacienda grande del sur de los Estados Unidos se conocía como _____ .

Columna II

a. siervos por contrato

b. un boicot

c. nativos

d. una plantación

e. misioneros

B. Ideas principales

Instrucciones: En cada espacio en blanco, escribe la letra que mejor conteste la pregunta.

_____ **6.** Los científicos creen que los primeros habitantes América del Norte de fueron los
    a. colonizadores británicos.   **c.** colonizadores franceses.
    b. nativos americanos.   **d.** exploradores holandeses.

_____ **7.** ¿Qué describe mejor los objetivos de los españoles y los franceses en América del Norte?
    a. Los españoles sólo querían el oro.   **c.** Ambos estaban interesados en obtener pieles.
    b. Los españoles querían apoderarse de la tierra, pero los franceses no.   **d.** Ni los españoles ni los franceses convirtieron a los nativos a su religión.

_____ **8.** Muchos ingleses llegaron a América del Norte para poseer tierra, de deudas y
    a. aprender el idioma de los nativos americanos.   **c.** tener libertad de religión.
    b. pelear contra los españoles y los franceses.   **d.** buscar oro y pieles.

_____ **9.** La causa de la guerra de los franceses y los nativos americanos fue
    a. la liberación de los colonizadores ingleses.
    b. los conflictos entre los nativos americanos y los franceses.
    c. la necesidad de cobrarle impuestos a los colonizadores americanos.
    d. el enfrentamiento por la obtención de terrenos entre la Gran Bretaña y Francia.

_____ **10.** ¿Qué era el Tratado de París?
    a. una carta para los colonizadores   **c.** un documento hallado en París
    b. un documento que le ponía fin a la guerra de los franceses y los nativos americanos   **d.** un documento que inspiró a los colonizadores americanos a luchar contra los británicos

Spanish Support

Crecimiento, expansión y Guerra Civil en los Estados Unidos

A. Durante la lectura

Instrucciones: A medida que vayas leyendo la Sección 2, completa la siguiente tabla con la información del crecimiento y la expansión de los Estados Unidos. Debajo de cada idea principal, escribe dos oraciones que la apoyen.

Idea principal A
Los Estados Unidos aumentó su territorio y nivel de desarrollo industrial durante la primera mitad del siglo XIX.
1. _____
2. _____
Idea principal B
La Guerra Civil que dividió a la nación fue el resultado de conflictos por el poder y la esclavitud.
3. _____
4. _____

B. Repaso de los términos clave

Instrucciones: En otra hoja de papel, escribe la definición de los siguientes términos clave.

5. La Compra de Luisiana

_____

6. destino manifiesto

_____

7. inmigrante

_____

8. revolución industrial

_____

9. abolicionista

_____

10. Guerra Civil

_____

11. reconstrucción

_____

12. segregar

_____

Nombre _____ Clase _____ Fecha _____

CAPÍTULO 2
LOS ESTADOS UNIDOS
Y EL CANADÁ
Forjados por
su historia

Crecimiento, expansión y Guerra Civil en los Estados Unidos

A. Términos y conceptos clave

Instrucciones: Empareja las definiciones de la Columna I con los términos de la Columna II. Escribe la letra correspondiente en cada espacio en blanco.

Columna I

_____ 1. persona que se traslada de un país a otro para residir allí

_____ 2. persona que quería terminar con la esclavitud

_____ 3. separar o apartar

_____ 4. plan para reedificar a los Estados Unidos después de la Guerra Civil

_____ 5. el cambio de la elaboración de productos con la ayuda de maquinaria

Columna II

a. abolicionista

b. reconstrucción

c. inmigrante

d. revolución industrial

e. segregar

B. Ideas principales

Instrucciones: En cada espacio en blanco, escribe la letra que mejor conteste la pregunta.

_____ 6. ¿Por qué La Compra de Luisiana fue importante para el desarrollo de los Estados Unidos?
   a. porque incitó la guerra de 1812
   b. porque duplicó el tamaño del país
   c. porque estableció el comercio con Francia
   d. porque aumentó la deuda del país

_____ 7. A medida que se formaban los nuevos estados americanos, así mismo obtenían el derecho de votar
   a. todos los ciudadanos.
   b. todos los hombres blancos mayores de 21 años.
   c. todos los hombres que poseían tierra.
   d. todas las mujeres y todos los afroamericanos.

_____ 8. ¿Qué oración describe mejor lo que el destino manifiesto significaba para muchos americanos en el siglo XIX?
   a. Los Estados Unidos tenían el derecho de poseer territorios en el Canadá.
   b. Los americanos tenían derecho a educación gratuita.
   c. Los Estados Unidos tenían derecho a poseer toda la tierra desde el Atlántico hasta el Pacífico.
   d. Los Estados Unidos era un nuevo hogar para los inmigrantes europeos.

_____ 9. ¿Por qué algunos países del sur no dejaron de ser parte de los Estados Unidos?
   a. porque querían comerciar de manera independiente con Inglaterra
   b. porque querían abolir la ley de esclavos fugitivos
   c. porque querían legalizar la esclavitud en el Canadá
   d. porque pensaban que el Presidente Lincoln iba a abolir la esclavitud

_____ 10. ¿Cuál fue uno de los efectos importantes de la Proclamación de Emancipación?
   a. Dio inicio a la reconstrucción.
   b. Muchos afroamericanos se unieron a la lucha contra el sur.
   c. Se estableció la segregación.
   d. Los estados del sur fundaron a los Estados Confederados de América.

Spanish Support

LECTURA DIRIGIDA Y REPASO

Estados Unidos se convierte en potencia mundial

A. Durante la lectura

Instrucciones: A medida que vayas leyendo la Sección 3, completa las siguientes preguntas en los espacios en blanco.

1. ¿Cómo afectó la revolución industrial a los pobres en los Estados Unidos?

_____

2. ¿Cómo se convirtió Estados Unidos en un jugador importante de los asuntos internacionales?

_____

3. ¿Cuál fue una razón por la que los Estados Unidos participó en la Primera Guerra Mundial?

_____

4. ¿Qué sucedió en 1929 y qué efecto tuvo?

_____

5. ¿Cuáles fueron dos conflictos que resultaron de la Guerra Fría?

_____

6. ¿Cuáles son algunos de los principales problemas que existen hoy en día en los Estados Unidos?

_____

B. Repaso de los términos clave

Instrucciones: Para completar cada oración, escribe el término correspondiente en el espacio en blanco.

7. A finales del siglo XIX, muchos inmigrantes llegaron a los Estados Unidos y formaron parte de la

_____ .

8. Jane Addams trabajó muy duro para crear una _____ en Chicago, para los inmigrantes pobres de la ciudad.

9. Bajo el _____ de 1862, el gobierno otorgó un pacel de tierra gratis a quien la cultivara y viviera en ella durante cinco años.

10. Durante la Primera Guerra Mundial, la Unión Soviética adoptó una forma de gobierno llamada

_____ .

11. La _____ duró cerca de 45 años y causó una tensión muy grande entre la Unión Soviética, los Estados Unidos y otros países.

12. El éxito del _____ en los Estados Unidos inspiró a otras personas además de los afroamericanos a luchar por sus derechos.

Nombre _____ Clase _____ Fecha _____

CAPÍTULO 2
LOS ESTADOS UNIDOS
Y EL CANADÁ
Forjados por
su historia

Estados Unidos se convierte en potencia mundial

A. Términos y conceptos clave

Instrucciones: Lee las oraciones a continuación. Si una oración es verdadera, escribe V en el espacio en blanco. Si es falsa, escribe F. En otra hoja de papel, vuelve a escribir las oraciones falsas para convertirlas en verdaderas.

_____ 1. Jane Addams creó una residencia comunitaria para los inmigrantes pobres de Chicago.

_____ 2. Bajo el comunismo, los ciudadanos particulares son dueños de toda la industria.

_____ 3. Martin Luther King Jr. fue uno de los primeros líderes del movimiento por los derechos civiles para acabar con la injusticia racial.

_____ 4. Después de la Segunda Guerra Mundial, se inició la Guerra Fría entre los Estados Unidos y Francia.

_____ 5. La disponibilidad de trabajadores en una sociedad se llama la fuerza laboral.

B. Ideas principales

Instrucciones: En cada espacio en blanco, escribe la letra que mejor conteste la pregunta.

_____ 6. ¿Por qué los Estados Unidos aprobó el Acta de Residencia?
   a. para darle tierra a los americanos en el Canadá
   b. para atraer colonos al oeste medio
   c. para animar a los inmigrantes a ir a los Estados Unidos
   d. para empezar el sistema de educación pública

_____ 7. Estados Unidos obtuvo el control de Puerto Rico, Guam y las islas Filipinas después de ganar
   a. la Primera Guerra Mundial.
   b. la Segunda Guerra Mundial.
   c. la guerra contra España.
   d. la Guerra Fría.

_____ 8. Los historiadores han identificado varios eventos que hicieron de los Estados Unidos una potencia mundial: la guerra contra España, la Primera Guerra Mundial y
   a. la Gran Depresión.
   b. la Segunda Guerra Mundial.
   c. los resplandecientes años veinte.
   d. el movimiento de los derechos civiles.

_____ 9. ¿Qué era el *New Deal*?
   a. el tratado que puso fin a la Segunda Guerra Mundial
   b. el final de la Guerra Fría
   c. el inicio de la Gran Depresión
   d. programas de gobierno para restaurar la economía

_____ 10. ¿Cuál fue el resultado directo del temor de los Estados Unidos a que la Unión Soviética expandiera su poder por todo el mundo?
   a. la Segunda Guerra Mundial
   b. la Guerra Fría
   c. el comunismo
   d. el Tratado de Versalles

Spanish Support

Crecimiento, expansión e independencia de el Canadá

A. Durante la lectura

Instrucciones: A medida que vayas leyendo la Sección 4, completa los espacios en blanco de las siguientes preguntas.

1. Al principio de la colonización de América del Norte, los franceses y los ingleses eran

    _____ .

2. El _____ le daba a los franceses de Quebec el derecho de hablar francés, practicar su religión y seguir sus costumbres.

3. Después de la revolución americana, la Gran Bretaña dividió al Canadá en dos colonias, el

    _____ y el _____ Canadá.

4. Hoy en día, el Alto Canadá se conoce como _____ , mientras que el Bajo Canadá

    se conoce como _____ .

5. En 1867, los canadienses obtuvieron el derecho de controlar su propio gobierno sin necesidad de

    una _____ .

6. Después de su "revolución pacífica", el Canadá vivió años de _____ .

7. Los canadienses participaron en la Primera Guerra Mundial, porque ellos aún eran

    _____ .

8. Después de la Segunda Guerra Mundial, los productos de las fábricas canadienses hallaron un

    mercado listo para consumir sus productos en _____ .

9. Las nuevas leyes aprobadas en 1969 explicaron las maneras de _____ la cultura y el estilo de vida de los francocanadienses.

10. Los cambios en la constitución canadiense significaban que el Canadá era totalmente

    _____ .

B. Repaso de los términos clave

Instrucciones: Para completar cada definición, escribe el término clave correspondiente en el espacio en blanco.

11. hablar o usar dos idiomas

    _____

12. región que no tiene un gobierno propio

    _____

CAPÍTULO 2
LOS ESTADOS UNIDOS Y EL CANADÁ
Forjados por su historia

Crecimiento, expansión e independencia de el Canadá

A. Términos y conceptos clave

Instrucciones: Empareja las definiciones de la Columna I con los términos de la Columna II. Escribe la letra correspondiente en cada espacio en blanco.

Columna I

_____ 1. Una región que tiene un gobierno propio es _____ .

_____ 2. Un país con dos idiomas oficiales _____ .

_____ 3. En 1837, _____ , un francocanadiense, organizó una rebelión en el Bajo Canadá.

_____ 4. El rebelde _____ dirigió a la población contra el gobierno británico en el Alto Canadá.

_____ 5. El rey inglés envió al _____ para hallar la manera de prevenir una rebelión en el Canadá.

Columna II

a. bilingüe

b. Louis Papineau

c. un dominio

d. Earl of Durham

e. William Mackenzie

B. Ideas principales

Instrucciones: En cada espacio en blanco, escribe la letra que mejor conteste la pregunta.

_____ 6. Francia e Inglaterra pelearon la guerra de los siete años, porque ambos países querían
    a. controlar el valle del Río Ohio.
    b. controlar a Quebec.
    c. controlar el Pacífico noroccidental.
    d. nuevas rutas de comercio.

_____ 7. ¿Cuál fué el resultado del Tratado de París?
    a. Los británicos pasaron el Acta de Quebec.
    b. La Gran Bretaña obtuvo el control de todo el Canadá.
    c. Todos los colonos franceses se fueron del Canadá.
    d. Francia obtuvo el control de casi todo el Canadá.

_____ 8. ¿Qué logró el Acta Británica de América del Norte?
    a. Canadá fue dividida en Alto y Bajo Canadá.
    b. Canadá se volvió una nación independiente.
    c. Canadá dejó de ser parte del dominio británico.
    d. Canadá paso a ser una nación que se gobierna a sí misma.

_____ 9. ¿Qué sucedió con el Canadá a causa de la victoria de los aliados en la Primera Guerra Mundial?
    a. Su economía sufrió.
    b. La Gran Bretaña tomó el control del gobierno canadiense.
    c. Se convirtió en potencia mundial.
    d. Sus ciudadanos dejaron de ser súbditos británicos.

_____ 10. ¿Cómo la constitución de 1982 cambió la vida en el Canadá?
    a. Estableció el inglés y el francés como idiomas oficiales.
    b. Estableció la independencia de Quebec.
    c. Estableció la independencia de Canadá.
    d. Estableció el inglés como el idioma oficial.

Spanish Support

Los Estados Unidos y el Canadá hoy en día: Socios y amigos

A. Durante la lectura

Instrucciones: A medida que vayas leyendo la Sección 5, completa la siguiente tabla con información sobre los distintos aspectos de los Estados Unidos y el Canadá.

Los Estados Unidos y el Canadá

Preocupaciones medioambientales	1. 2. 3.
Lazos económicos	4. 5.

B. Repaso de los términos clave

Instrucciones: En otra hoja de papel, escribe la definición de los siguientes términos clave.

6. combustible fósil

_____

7. lluvia ácida

_____

8. despeje forestal

_____

9. interdependiente

_____

10. tarifa

_____

11. libre comercio

_____

12. NAFTA

_____

Nombre _____ Clase _____ Fecha _____

CAPÍTULO 2
LOS ESTADOS UNIDOS Y EL CANADÁ
Forjados por
su historia

Los Estados Unidos y el Canadá hoy en día: Socios y amigos

A. Términos y conceptos clave

Instrucciones: Empareja las definiciones de la Columna I con los términos de la Columna II. Escribe la letra correspondiente en cada espacio en blanco.

Columna I

_____ 1. gasolina o carbón

_____ 2. cortar todos los árboles de una zona

_____ 3. característica de los países que tienen que hacer negocios entre sí para tener éxito

_____ 4. derechos especiales que cobra un gobierno por mercancía importada

_____ 5. acuerdo comercial firmado por el Canadá, México y los Estados Unidos

Columna II

a. interdependiente

b. tarifa

c. combustible fósil

d. NAFTA

e. despeje forestal

B. Ideas principales

Instrucciones: En cada espacio en blanco, escribe la letra que mejor conteste la pregunta.

_____ 6. ¿Qué sucedió en 1969 como consecuencia del incendio del Río Cuyahoga?
   a. Los Estados Unidos y la Gran Bretaña crearon leyes para la protección del medio ambiente.
   b. Los Estados Unidos y el Canadá cooperaron en la limpieza del Lago Erie.
   c. Aumentó la polución.
   d. Aumentó la polución del agua.

_____ 7. ¿Cómo afecta la lluvia ácida al medio ambiente?
   a. Extermina plantas y árboles.   **c.** Aumenta la cantidad de lluvia.
   b. Hace disminuir la temperatura.   **d.** Purifica el aire.

_____ 8. ¿Por qué la lluvia ácida causada por las plantas de energía de los Estados Unidos es un problema para el Canadá?
   a. Las plantas de energía de los Estados Unidos proveen energía para los dos países.
   b. Los peces de los Estados Unidos son desviados al Canadá.
   c. Los canadienses beben agua que es embotellada en los Estados Unidos.
   d. El viento desplaza el aire contaminado desde los Estados Unidos hacia el Canadá.

_____ 9. Las exclusas, los canales y las represas de la ruta marítima del Río San Lorenzo permiten a los barcos desplazarse
   a. al mismo nivel del agua.   **c.** hacia el Océano Pacífico.
   b. por el Río Misisipí hacia el sur.   **d.** de un nivel del agua a otro.

_____ 10. ¿Cuáles fueron las consecuencias del acuerdo para eliminar tarifas entre los Estados Unidos y el Canadá?
   a. Disminuyó el crecimiento económico.   **c.** Aumentó el comercio entre los dos países.
   b. Se eliminó el libre comercio.   **d.** Aumentó el comercio entre los Estados Unidos y México.

Spanish Support

Nombre _____ Clase _____ Fecha _____

LOS ESTADOS UNIDOS Y EL CANADÁ
Forjados por su historia

Preguntas guía:

- ¿Cómo han afectado los eventos históricos a las culturas de los Estados Unidos y el Canadá?
- ¿Cómo son diferentes los gobiernos de los Estados Unidos y Canadá? ¿Cómo se parecen?

<u>Los científicos creen que los primeros habitantes de América del Norte emigraron de Asia hace unos 30,000 años.</u> Los nativos americanos eventualmente poblaron todos los rincones del continente. Después de la llegada de los europeos, la forma de vida de los nativos empezó a cambiar. Los europeos los desplazaron de sus tierras y los obligaron a trabajar en minas y granjas. Miles de ellos murieron debido a las condiciones tan severas y a las enfermedades traídas por los europeos.

<u>A lo largo de la costa Atlántica, los colonizadores ingleses establecieron 13 colonias.</u> Con el tiempo, protestaron contra el control del gobierno británico. Ese conflicto los llevó a la guerra de la independencia, que tuvo como consecuencia la independencia de los Estados Unidos de la Gran Bretaña. Durante la primera mitad del siglo XIX, los Estados Unidos obtuvo nuevos territorios. Hubo un enorme crecimiento industrial en las ciudades del noreste. Además, los granjeros del sur también prosperaron. Sin embargo, el tema de la esclavitud dividió el norte y el sur. Eso condujo a la Guerra Civil. La guerra duró cuatro años y desgarró al país. Cuando la guerra terminó, comenzó un período de reconstrucción.

<u>Durante la segunda mitad del siglo XIX, llegaron a los Estados Unidos millones de inmigrantes. Además, el país expandió sus fronteras.</u> La participación en las dos guerras mundiales ayudó a hacer de los Estados Unidos una potencia mundial. Después de la Segunda Guerra Mundial hubo una gran tensión entre los Estados Unidos y la Unión Soviética. A ese período se le llamó la Guerra Fría. Dentro del país, el movimiento por los derechos civiles cuestionó la segregación entre los afroamericanos y los blancos. Eventualmente, las leyes fueron cambiadas para darles a todos los americanos los mismos derechos.

<u>Durante la expansión europea del territorio canadiense, los franceses y los ingleses eran rivales.</u> Los franceses deseaban crear un país independiente en Quebec. Eso nunca ocurrió, así que la tensión entre los canadienses franceses y los canadienses ingleses prevalece aún hoy en día. Hasta 1837, el Canadá fue gobernada por la Gran Bretaña. Después de fallar en dos intentos por rebelarse, finalmente los canadienses obtuvieron el derecho de gobernarse a sí mismos. Durante la Primera Guerra Mundial y la Segunda Guerra Mundial, los canadienses fortalecieron su industria para convertirse en una de las naciones industrializadas líder a nivel mundial. En 1982, una nueva constitución hizo del Canadá un país bilingüe y completamente independiente de la Gran Bretaña.

<u>Hoy en día, a los Estados Unidos y al Canadá los une sus economías. Cada uno representa para el otro el socio comercial más importante.</u> El Tratado de Libre Comercio (NAFTA) fortaleció los lazos comerciales entre los dos países. También estableció el libre comercio entre los Estados Unidos, el Canadá y México. Los Estados Unidos y el Canadá han trabajado juntos para resolver los problemas del medio ambiente que tienen en común. Juntos construyeron la ruta marítima de San Lorenzo.

LOS ESTADOS UNIDOS Y EL CANADÁ
Forjados por su historia

CAPÍTULO
2

Instrucciones: Empareja las definiciones de la Columna I con los términos clave de la Columna II. Escribe la letra correspondiente en cada espacio en blanco. Si es necesario, mira los términos en el glosario de tu libro de texto.

Columna I

_____ **1.** hablar dos idiomas

_____ **2.** ley que otorgaba tierra en las llanuras del oeste medio de los Estados Unidos a todo adulto que deseara cultivarla durante cinco años

_____ **3.** originarios de un lugar particular

_____ **4.** rehusar a comprar o usar ciertos productos o servicios

_____ **5.** tipo de explotación de bosques en el que se cortan todos los árboles de una zona

_____ **6.** persona que se oponía a la práctica de la esclavitud

_____ **7.** el comercio sin restricciones entre naciones

_____ **8.** grupo de personas que se unieron para apoyar la igualdad de derechos de todas las minorías

_____ **9.** derechos cobrados por importaciones

_____ **10.** persona que debe trabajar por algunos años para obtener su libertad

_____ **11.** período de tensión entre los Estados Unidos y la Unión Soviética

_____ **12.** período de transición de la elaboración de productos a mano, a la elaboración de productos con la ayuda de maquinaria

_____ **13.** plan después de la Guerra Civil para tratar de reedificar a los Estados Unidos

_____ **14.** centro comunitario para inmigrantes pobres

_____ **15.** la creencia de que los Estados Unidos debería poseer y gobernar todo el territorio de América del Norte entre el Océano Atlántico y el Océano Pacífico

Columna II

a. abolicionista

b. lluvia ácida

c. bilingüe

d. boicot

e. movimiento por los derechos civiles

f. despeje forestal

g. Guerra Fría

h. dominio

i. libre comercio

j. Acta de Residencia

k. siervo por contrato

l. nativo

m. revolución industrial

n. La Compra de Luisiana

o. destino manifiesto

p. misionero

q. reconstrucción

r. residencia comunitaria

s. tarifa

Spanish Support

CARTA PARA LA FAMILIA

Las culturas de los Estados Unidos y el Canadá

La Línea Abierta de Ciencias Sociales

Querida familia:

Ahora que ya estamos familiarizados con la historia de los Estados Unidos y del Canadá, vamos a estudiar más a fondo las culturas de estas dos naciones. Nuestra clase aprenderá cómo los nativos americanos, los europeos y los inmigrantes de todo el mundo han hecho contribuciones únicas y han influido en la cultura de maneras particulares.

Probablemente su hijo o hija tendrá muchas preguntas sobre las culturas estadounidense y canadiense. Un inuit (o esquimal) en el ártico, un francocanadiense en Montreal, un mexicoamericano en Texas y un agricultor suecoamericano en Minnesota probablemente contestarían las mismas preguntas de maneras diferentes. Para ayudar a su hijo o hija con las preguntas que tenga, usted puede compartir sus propias ideas. Conversen sobre la experiencias de sus ancestros. Él o ella le podrían hacer preguntas como: ¿Cómo llegaron ellos a los Estados Unidos? ¿De dónde venían? ¿Vivían ellos aquí cuando llegaron los primeros europeos? De otra manera, ¿cómo hicieron para acostumbrarse a la vida en el nuevo país? ¿Qué elementos culturales trajeron consigo?

Otro aspecto importante de ambos países es cómo las culturas se han mezclado a través de su historia. Usted y su hijo o hija pueden ver los efectos de las distintas culturas en áreas como: la música, las artes gráficas, los alimentos, los deportes, las películas y el comercio. Busque con su hijo o hija ejemplos de mezcla cultural, y ayúdele a identificar las fuentes culturales de lo que hallen.

A medida que escuche, lea o vea informes en las noticias, ayude a su hijo o hija a pensar en cómo se podrían sentir los miembros de distintos grupos étnicos de ser ciudadanos estadounidenses o canadienses. ¿Qué retos y problemas tienen que enfrentar? ¿Cómo podrían sobrellevar esos retos y problemas?

Gracias por su ayuda. Espero que este estudio de los Estados Unidos y el Canadá sea una experiencia estimulante y divertida tanto para usted como para su hijo o hija.

Atentamente,

CAPÍTULO 3
Las culturas de los Estados Unidos y el Canadá

Los Estados Unidos: Una nación de inmigrantes

A. Durante la lectura

Instrucciones: A medida que vayas leyendo la Sección 1, completa las siguientes oraciones.

1. Las culturas de los primeros americanos reflejaba su _____ .

2. Antes de que los exploradores españoles llegaran a América, no había _____ .

3. Los colonos rusos llevaron consigo al ocstc medio de los Estados Unidos un tipo de _____ que era más resistente.

4. Los inmigrantes tienen que decidir que cosas de su _____ deben conservar y que cosas deben _____ .

5. Casi todos los inmigrantes se apegan a cosas que les hacen recordar sus _____ .

6. Conservar las costumbres les da a los inmigrantes un sentido de _____ en el nuevo país.

7. El intercambio de aspectos tales como los estilos musicales, ayuda a apreciar la _____ de la vida en los Estados Unidos.

8. Con frecuencia, los aspectos de la vida diaria aparecen en el trabajo de los _____ .

9. Las culturas de todo el mundo han influenciado el _____ estadounidense.

B. Repaso de los términos clave

Instrucciones: Escribe el término clave correspondiente para cada una de las siguientes definiciones.

10. proceso en el que diferentes culturas comparten ideas y formas de hacer las cosas

_____

11. grupo de personas que pueden tener en común un mismo lenguaje, religión y tradiciones culturales

_____

12. gran variedad de culturas

_____

Nombre _____ Clase _____ Fecha _____

Una nación de inmigrantes

CAPÍTULO 3
Las culturas de los
Estados Unidos
y el Canadá

A. Términos y conceptos clave

Instrucciones: Empareja las definiciones de la Columna I con los términos de la Columna II.
Escribe la letra correspondiente en cada espacio en blanco.

Columna I

_____ **1.** proceso en el que diferentes culturas comparten ideas y formas de hacer las cosas

_____ **2.** grupo de personas que puede tener en común un mismo lenguaje, religión y tradiciones culturales

_____ **3.** gran variedad de culturas

_____ **4.** persona que llega a un país proveniente de otro, con la intención de establecerse allí

_____ **5.** variedad de accidentes geográficos, clima y vegetación

Columna II

a. grupo étnico

b. inmigrante

c. intercambio cultural

d. diversidad geográfica

e. diversidad cultural

B. Ideas principales

Instrucciones: En cada espacio en blanco, escribe la letra que mejor conteste la pregunta.

_____ **6.** ¿Cuál era una manera tradicional en la que los grupos nativos americanos compartían sus ideas entre sí?
    a. a través de los libros   **c.** a través de la agricultura
    b. a través del comercio   **d.** a través del cuidado de bosques

_____ **7.** ¿Qué oración describe mejor el intercambio cultural entre los nativos americanos y los primeros colonos europeos?
    a. Los europeos se rehusaban a ser influenciados por la cultura de los nativos americanos.
    b. Los nativos americanos se rehusaban a ser influenciados por la cultura de los europeos.
    c. Tanto los europeos como los nativos americanos cambiaron su forma de vida.
    d. Los europeos cambiaron la forma de vida de los nativos americanos.

_____ **8.** ¿Cómo deben cambiar los inmigrantes cuando se establecen en otro país?
    a. Deben renunciar a todas sus costumbres.
    b. Deben aprender el idioma y las costumbres del nuevo país.
    c. Deben ignorar a otros inmigrantes.
    d. Deben negarse a hablar el idioma del nuevo país.

_____ **9.** En los Estados Unidos los pasatiempos, los alimentos, el acento al hablar y la música
    a. son iguales en todas partes.   **c.** son originarios de Rusia.
    b. varían de región en región.   **d.** son iguales que en el Canadá.

_____ **10.** Los Estados Unidos es un país con diversidad cultural, porque
    a. tiene un solo grupo étnico.   **c.** es muy grande.
    b. muchos inmigrantes viven allí.   **d.** la mayoría de las personas viven en las ciudades.

CAPÍTULO 3
**Las culturas de los
Estados Unidos
y el Canadá**

El Canadá: Un mosaico

A. Durante la lectura

Instrucciones: A medida que vayas leyendo la Sección 2, completa la siguiente tabla con información sobre la cultura del Canadá.

Los habitantes y la cultura del Canadá

Los medios de comunicación	1.
Los francocanadienses	2.
	3.
Los nativos americanos	4.
	5.
Las artes	6.
	7.
Los deportes	8.
	9.

B. Repaso de los términos clave

Instrucciones: En el espacio en blanco, escribe la definición del siguiente término clave.

10. reserva

_____

Spanish Support

Nombre _____ Clase _____ Fecha _____

EXAMEN DE LA SECCIÓN

CAPÍTULO 3
Las culturas de los
Estados Unidos
y el Canadá

El Canadá: Un mosaico

A. Términos y conceptos clave

Instrucciones: Empareja las definiciones de la Columna I con los términos de la Columna II.
Escribe la letra correspondiente en cada espacio en blanco.

Columna I

_____ **1.** En las décadas de 1920 y de 1930, _____ desarrolló
nuevas técnicas para pintar paisajes del Canadá.

_____ **2.** Una zona que el gobierno ha separado para que
vivan los nativos se llama _____ .

_____ **3.** Los inuit llaman a su nuevo territorio _____ .

_____ **4.** El cantante canadiense de música folklórica, _____ ,
escribió *"The Wreck of the Edmund Fitzgerald"*.

_____ **5.** Los críticos han aclamado a la escritora canadiense
_____ .

Columna II

a. Nunavut

b. Margaret Atwood

c. el grupo de los siete

d. Gordon Lightfoot

e. reserva

B. Ideas principales

Instrucciones: En cada espacio en blanco, escribe la letra que mejor conteste la pregunta.

_____ **6.** Los dos idiomas oficiales del Canadá son
   a. el chino y el francés.   **c.** el inglés y el chino.
   b. el inglés y el francés.   **d.** el francés y el español.

_____ **7.** ¿Cómo demuestran muchos francocanadienses su preocupación por preservar su herencia
cultural?
   a. Quieren convertir a Quebec en colonia de Francia.
   b. Quieren que el francés sea el idioma oficial del Canadá.
   c. Quieren adoptar la constitución francesa.
   d. Quieren convertir a Quebec en un país independiente.

_____ **8.** Para conservar la cultura de los nativos americanos, el gobierno canadiense aprobó leyes que
les permiten
   a. crear una nación independiente.
   b. vivir en reservas.
   c. hacer de sus idiomas los idiomas oficiales del país.
   d. usar su propio idioma en las escuelas.

_____ **9.** ¿Cómo ayudó el gobierno canadiense a los inuit (o esquimales) a recuperar su identidad
cultural?
   a. Les concedió tierras.   **c.** Les enseño actividades tradicionales.
   b. Los obligó a vivir en ciudades grandes.   **d.** Los obligó a comprar alimentos.

_____ **10.** ¿Qué aspecto cultural une a la mayoría de los canadienses?
   a. la influencia de la cultura francesa   **c.** la influencia de los inuit
   b. la influencia de la cultura estadounidense   **d.** la influencia de los Chippewa

Las culturas de los Estados Unidos y el Canadá

Preguntas guía:

- ¿Cómo han afectado los eventos históricos a las culturas de los Estados Unidos y el Canadá?
- ¿Cómo la diversidad de habitantes de los Estados Unidos y el Canadá ha beneficiado y afectado a ambos países?

La zona que hoy en día llamamos los Estados Unidos siempre ha sido culturalmente diversa. Las culturas de los primeros americanos reflejaban el medio ambiente en que vivían. Cuando los europeos llegaron, cambiaron la forma de vida de los nativos. Los europeos trajeron caballos y herramientas de metal. Los nativos también aportaron muchas cosas a los europeos, incluyendo los métodos de caza y la manera de sobrevivir en el bosque. A través de la historia de los Estados Unidos, ha ocurrido un intercambio cultural entre los distintos grupos que han vivido allí.

La mayoría de los inmigrantes se apegan a algunas de sus costumbres tradicionales. De esa manera, pueden conservar un sentido de identidad en esa nueva tierra. Al mismo tiempo, han ayudado a enriquecer la cultura estadounidense. Artistas, escritores y músicos combinan aspectos de la cultura estadounidense con elementos de otras culturas del mundo.

El Canadá también es un país muy diverso. Podemos apreciar su diversidad en una estación radial de la ciudad de Toronto que transmite programas en 30 idiomas distintos. Uno de los grupos étnicos más grande, los francocanadienses de Quebec, quieren separarse del Canadá y formar su propio país. Ellos han luchado para que el gobierno canadiense reconozca y respete su herencia cultural y su idioma. Su empeño hizo que el Canadá se convirtiera en un país bilingüe, donde los idiomas oficiales son el inglés y el francés.

Los nativos del Canadá también quieren conservar sus culturas. Los colonizadores europeos se apropiaron de las tierras de los nativos y los obligaron a vivir en reservas. Hoy en día, los nativos quieren que les devuelvan las tierras que les quitaron o que los recompensen económicamente por ellas. Los inuit han logrado convencer al gobierno para que les conceda un terreno extenso, en lo que eran los Territorios del Noroeste. A ese, su nuevo territorio, lo llaman *Nunavut* o "Nuestra Tierra".

A muchos canadienses les preocupa la gran influencia que tienen los Estados Unidos en su cultura. Debido a eso, han hecho grandes esfuerzos para promover la cultura canadiense. La Comisión Nacional de Cine del Canadá (*The National Film Board*) apoya películas con temas nacionales. El Canadá tiene muchos artistas, escritores y músicos que se concentran en aspectos que son únicos de la cultura canadiense. Por ejemplo, los impresores y escultores inuit, crean imágenes que provienen de ideas tradicionales.

ACTIVIDAD DE VOCABULARIO

Las culturas de los Estados Unidos y el Canadá

Instrucciones: Empareja los términos clave de la tabla con las definiciones de abajo. Escribe la letra correspondiente en cada espacio en blanco. Luego escribe una oración que use el término o la forma plural del término en el espacio respectivo. Si es necesario, observa los términos en el glosario de tu libro de texto o fíjate cómo se usan en el Capítulo 3.

a. grupo étnico	**c.** reserva
b. intercambio cultural	**d.** bilingüe

_____ **1.** proceso en el que diferentes culturas comparten ideas y formas de hacer las cosas

_____

_____

_____

_____ **2.** zonas separadas por el gobierno canadiense para los pueblos nativos

_____

_____

_____

_____ **3.** alguien que habla dos idiomas; que tiene dos idiomas oficiales

_____

_____

_____

_____ **4.** grupo de personas que pueden tener en común un mismo lenguaje, religión y tradiciones culturales

_____

_____

_____

Exploremos los Estados Unidos

La Línea Abierta de Ciencias Sociales

Querida familia:

Como parte de nuestro estudio continuo de los Estados Unidos, vamos a explorar las regiones de los Estados Unidos. Durante los próximos días, estudiaremos cuatro zonas: el noreste, el sur, el oeste medio y el oeste. De cada una de esas regiones, estudiaremos su historia, crecimiento, desarrollo y los retos que enfrentan hoy en día.

Para ayudar a su hijo o hija en nuestro estudio, podrían hablar juntos acerca de la región del país en la que viven. Puede hacerle preguntas como: ¿En qué se diferencia nuestra región de otras regiones? ¿Qué regiones son similares a la nuestra? ¿Qué eventos históricos son importantes para nuestra comunidad y sus alrededores? Si hay una asociación de la historia local, podría comunicarse con ellos para pedirles información acerca de los primeros pobladores de la región.

A medida que su hijo o hija lea acerca de otros lugares del país, usted podría buscar artículos de periódicos o informes sobre varios temas regionales, para ayudarle a expandir esos conocimientos. Por ejemplo, usted podría compartir información sobre la bolsa y el mercado de acciones de Nueva York o sobre las actividades del gobierno en Washington, D.C. También podría buscar informes que traten de los últimos avances en la agricultura, las distintas industrias en el sur, o el uso y la administración de los recursos naturales en el oeste.

Converse con su hijo o hija acerca de los retos que enfrentan las ciudades con el crecimiento de la población, y de cómo este crecimiento nos puede conducir a un estado de sobrepoblación y, a su vez, a una gran demanda de recursos. Concentren su conversación en la manera en que tratan esos retos en su zona. Podría también hablar con amigos o familiares que hayan tenido algunos de esos problemas en zonas más urbanas o rurales que las nuestras, puede que ellos estén dispuestos a compartir experiencias personales diferentes a la suya.

Espero que tanto usted como su hijo o hija disfruten de este estudio detallado de las regiones de los Estados Unidos.

Atentamente,

Spanish Support

El noreste
Tierra de grandes ciudades

A. Durante la lectura

Instrucciones: A medida que vayas leyendo la Sección 1, escribe tus respuestas a las siguientes preguntas en los espacios en blanco.

1. ¿Cuáles son algunos medios de transporte de la ciudad de Nueva York?

_____

2. ¿Qué es la megalópolis del Noreste?

_____

3. ¿Dónde quedan los centros económicos del noreste?

_____

4. ¿Por qué se conoce a Filadelfia como una potencia industrial?

_____

5. ¿Cuáles son algunas de las cosas por las que Boston es famosa?

_____

6. ¿Por qué la ciudad de Nueva York es descrita como "la capital financiera" del país?

_____

7. ¿Cuál fue el primer lugar al que llegaron millones de inmigrantes que llegaron a los Estados Unidos entre 1892 y 1943?

_____

B. Repaso de los términos clave

Instrucciones: En los espacios en blanco a continuación, escribe las definiciones para los siguientes términos clave.

8. viajes cotidianos

_____

9. megalópolis

_____

10. densidad de población

_____

CAPÍTULO 4
Exploremos los
Estados Unidos

El noroeste
Tierra de grandes ciudades

A. Términos y conceptos clave

Instrucciones: Empareja las definiciones de la Columna I con los términos de la Columna II.
Escribe la letra correspondiente en cada espacio en blanco.

Columna I

_____ 1. la rutina diaria de ir y volver del trabajo

_____ 2. ciudades y centros urbanos que forman juntos una extensa zona urbana

_____ 3. número promedio de personas por milla cuadrada

_____ 4. la ciudad en la que los colonos americanos adoptaron la Declaración de Independencia

_____ 5. la capital financiera de los Estados Unidos

Columna II

a. densidad de población

b. Filadelfia

c. viajes cotidianos

d. la ciudad de Nueva York

e. megalópolis

B. Ideas principales

Instrucciones: En cada espacio en blanco, escribe la letra que mejor conteste la pregunta.

_____ 6. ¿Cuál es la región más densamente poblada de los Estados Unidos?
    a. el sur
    b. el noroeste
    c. el noreste
    d. el este

_____ 7. Los centros financieros del noreste son
    a. las granjas.
    b. las pescaderías.
    c. los bosques.
    d. las ciudades.

_____ 8. ¿Qué factor contribuyó a hacer de Filadelfia un importante centro industrial?
    a. su ubicación en el Río Delaware
    b. su tamaño pequeño
    c. sus extensos terrenos agrícolas
    d. sus famosas universidades científicas y tecnológicas

_____ 9. Desde 1892 hasta 1943 el primer lugar al que llegaban los inmigrantes que entraban a los Estados Unidos era
    a. Washington, D.C.
    b. las ciudades del oeste medio.
    c. las ciudades porteñas del noreste.
    d. las ciudades del sur.

_____ 10. La zona de Boston es famosa por tener más de veinte
    a. parques.
    b. universidades.
    c. tiendas de muebles.
    d. centros médicos.

Spanish Support

El sur
Un paisaje en continuo cambio

A. Durante la lectura

Instrucciones: A medida que vayas leyendo la Sección 2, completa la siguiente tabla con información sobre el sur de los Estados Unidos. Debajo de cada idea principal, escribe dos ideas que la apoyen.

El continuo cambio del sur

La agricultura	1.	2.
La industria	3.	4.
El transporte y el turismo	5.	6.
Atlanta y Washington, D.C.	7.	8.

B. Repaso de los términos clave

Instrucciones: Para completar cada oración, escribe el término correspondiente en el espacio en blanco.

9. Productos como el plástico, la pintura y el asfalto, también son llamados _____ .

10. El sur de los Estados Unidos también se conoce con el nombre de _____ .

11. La transición de una economía basada en la agricultura a una economía basada en la industria se llama _____ .

El sur
Un paisaje en continuo cambio

A. Términos y conceptos clave

Instrucciones: Lee las oraciones a continuación. Si una oración es verdadera, escribe V en el espacio en blanco. Si es falsa, escribe F. En otra hoja de papel, vuelve a escribir las oraciones falsas para convertirlas en verdaderas.

_____ 1. Los petroquímicos son sustancias derivadas del petróleo, como el plástico, la pintura y el asfalto.

_____ 2. Atlanta es una de las regiones de menor crecimiento en el noroeste de los Estados Unidos.

_____ 3. La industrialización es la transición de una economía basada en la industria a una economía basada en la agricultura.

_____ 4. El sur forma parte del "cinturón soleado".

_____ 5. Washington, D.C., está ubicado en Virginia.

B. Ideas principales

Instrucciones: En cada espacio en blanco, escribe la letra que mejor conteste la pregunta.

_____ 6. Los colonizadores pudieron cultivar algodón en el sur gracias a
    a. la riqueza de la región.
    b. la geografía, el clima y la tierra fértil de la región.
    c. el tamaño de la región.
    d. su cercanía al Océano Atlántico.

_____ 7. En Luisiana, Oklahoma y Texas, hay compañías que hacen perforaciones para buscar
    a. agua.   **c.** plásticos y pintura.
    b. oro.   **d.** petróleo y gas natural.

_____ 8. ¿Por qué son tan importantes para el sur las fábricas de textiles?
    a. porque producen telas   **c.** porque procesan minerales
    b. porque producen petroquímicos   **d.** porque atraen al turismo

_____ 9. Dos puertos importantes en el sur son
    a. Atlanta, Georgia y Washington, D.C.
    b. Raleigh, Carolina del Norte y Austin, Texas.
    c. Miami, Florida y Nueva Orléans, Luisiana.
    d. Nueva York, Neuva York y Filadelfia, Pennsylvania.

_____ 10. Washington, D.C. está ubicado
    a. en el noreste.
    b. entre Maryland y Virginia.
    c. entre Carolina del Norte y Carolina del Sur.
    d. en Georgia.

Spanish Support

El oeste medio
Más allá de la agricultura

A. Durante la lectura

Instrucciones: A medida que vayas leyendo la Sección 3, completa la siguiente tabla con información sobre el medio oeste. Debajo de cada idea principal, escribe tres ideas que la apoyen.

Idea principal A
La mayoría de las granjas familiares del oeste medio han sido reemplazadas por haciendas corporativas.

1. _____

2. _____

3. _____

Idea principal B
La disminución de trabajadores en el campo ha causado el aumento de la población en las ciudades del oeste medio.

4. _____

5. _____

6. _____

B. Repaso de los términos clave

Instrucciones: En los espacios en blanco a continuación, escribe las definiciones para los siguientes términos clave.

7. hacienda de cultivos mixtos

_____

8. recesión

_____

9. hacienda corporativa

_____

CAPÍTULO 4
Exploremos los
Estados Unidos

El oeste medio
Más allá de la agricultura

A. Términos y conceptos clave

Instrucciones: Empareja las definiciones de la Columna I con los términos de la Columna II.
Escribe la letra correspondiente en cada espacio en blanco.

Columna I

_____ 1. Diferentes tipos de cultivos son producidos en
una _____ .

_____ 2. Una caída drástica de la actividad comercial es
una _____ .

_____ 3. Muchas granjas pequeñas se pueden combinar para
formar una _____ .

_____ 4. La ciudad más grande en el medio oeste es _____ .

_____ 5. Una ciudad del oeste medio, _____ , Misuri, fue el
punto de partida para los pioneros en dirección oeste.

Columna II

a. recesión

b. Chicago

c. hacienda corporativa

d. hacienda de cultivos mixtos

e. San Luis

B. Ideas principales

Instrucciones: En cada espacio en blanco, escribe la letra que mejor conteste la pregunta.

_____ 6. ¿Por qué se conoce al oeste medio como el "heartland" (el corazón) de los Estados Unidos?
   a. porque es el centro nacional del transporte
   b. porque es el centro nacional de las comunicaciones
   c. porque es el centro nacional de la agricultura
   d. porque es el centro nacional de las finanzas

_____ 7. Desde 1980, muchos agricultores han vendido o abandonado sus granjas debido a
   a. la recesión económica.
   b. un aumento en las haciendas
       de cultivos mixtos.
   c. un aumento en la demanda.
   d. un aumento en los productos
       de exportación.

_____ 8. ¿Qué sucedió con las granjas familiares que fueron vendidas antes de 1980?
   a. Las granjas pequeñas fueron vendidas a otras granjas familiares.
   b. Las granjas pequeñas fueron reemplazadas por fábricas.
   c. Las granjas pequeñas fueron combinadas con otras para formar haciendas corporativas.
   d. Las granjas pequeñas fueron reemplazadas por grandes almacenes.

_____ 9. ¿Por qué Chicago fue un centro de manufactura a finales del siglo XIX?
   a. Porque era la capital de los Estados Unidos
   b. Porque estaba cerca de las principales rutas de transporte
   c. porque era la ciudad más poblada de los Estados Unidos
   d. Porque muchos bancos estaban ubicados allí

_____ 10. ¿En qué ciudad del oeste medio hallarías el centro de operaciones de la industria automotriz de
los Estados Unidos?
   a. San Luis
   b. Minneapolis-Saint Paul
   c. Detroit
   d. Chicago

Spanish Support

LECTURA DIRIGIDA Y REPASO

El oeste: El uso inteligente de sus recursos

A. Durante la lectura

Instrucciones: A medida que vayas leyendo la Sección 4, completa las siguientes oraciones.

1. Teodoro Roosevelt comprendió que los enormes recursos naturales del oeste no durarían sin

_____ .

2. La increible riqueza de los _____ ha atraido personas al oeste por más de 400 años.

3. Con la fiebre del oro en California de 1849, la _____ de la región aumentó enormemente de un día para otro.

4. Después de la Guerra Civil, los colonos hallaron madera para construir casas en el

_____ .

5. Para proteger algunas zonas de territorio virgen en el oeste, el congreso creó varios

_____ .

6. La mayoría de los habitantes del oeste de hoy en día trabajan y viven en _____ .

7. Portland, Oregón se convirtió en el centro del comercio de _____ ,

_____ , _____ , y _____ .

8. La zona alrededor de San José, California es llamado _____ , porque allí hay muchas empresas de computadores.

B. Repaso de los términos clave

Instrucciones: Para completar cada definición, escribe el término clave correspondiente en el espacio en blanco.

9. uno de los primeros mineros que llegaron a California durante la fiebre del oro

_____

10. sistema de buses y trenes usados como transporte

_____

CAPÍTULO 4
Exploremos los
Estados Unidos

El oeste: El uso inteligente de sus recursos

A. Términos y conceptos clave

Instrucciones: Empareja las definiciones de la Columna I con los términos de la Columna II.
Escribe la letra correspondiente en cada espacio en blanco.

Columna I

_____ **1.** los primeros mineros durante la fiebre del oro

_____ **2.** lugar donde ocurrió la fiebre del oro en California

_____ **3.** sistema eficiente de transporte que reemplaza a los automóviles por buses y trenes

_____ **4.** centro del comercio de madera, pieles, granos, salmón y lana en Oregón

_____ **5.** ciudad cerca al "Valle de la Silicona"

Columna II

a. la Sierra Nevada

b. Portland

c. los *forty niners*

d. transporte masivo

e. San José

B. Ideas principales

Instrucciones: En cada espacio en blanco, escribe la letra que mejor conteste la pregunta.

_____ **6.** Los primeros colonos que llegaron al oeste fueron atraidos por
   a. sus recursos naturales.   **c.** sus fuentes de energía.
   b. sus industrias.   **d.** sus ciudades.

_____ **7.** ¿Cuál fue uno de los efectos de la fiebre del oro en California?
   a. San Francisco se convirtió en una ciudad de mucha prosperidad.
   b. Se fundó Portland.
   c. Se cerró el parque nacional de Yosemite.
   d. Boston se convirtió en un centro de comercio importante.

_____ **8.** ¿Por qué el congreso hizo crear varios bosques y parques nacionales?
   a. para disminuir las congestiones de tráfico de la región
   b. para reducir la polución ambiental
   c. para proteger algunas zonas del oeste y conservarlas como territorio virgen
   d. para atraer a un gran número de turistas

_____ **9.** Portland atrajo muchas industrias manufactureras gracias
   a. a la agricultura.   **c.** al bajo costo de la electricidad.
   b. a la minería.   **d.** a la pesca.

_____ **10.** Algunos de los problemas que enfrentan las ciudades del oeste debido al crecimiento de las ciudades es la polución del agua, las congestiones de tráfico y
   a. menos casas nuevas.   **c.** una disminución de la polución.
   b. una menor industria.   **d.** la polución ambiental.

Spanish Support

RESUMEN DEL CAPÍTULO

CAPÍTULO 4

Exploremos los Estados Unidos

Preguntas guía:

- ¿Cómo han afectado los eventos históricos a la cultura de los Estados Unidos y del Canadá?
- ¿Cómo se conviertieron los Estados Unidos y Canadá en dos de los países más ricos del mundo?

Podemos dividir a los Estados Unidos en cuatro regiones: el noreste, el sur, el oeste medio y el oeste. Cada una de esas regiones tiene su propia geografía, historia, economía y cultura.

El noreste es la región más poblada de los Estados Unidos. La actividad económica del noreste está centrada en las ciudades de la región. Filadelfia es importante por su industria. Boston es famosa por sus compañías de alta tecnología y sus universidades. Nueva York es el centro de las instituciones financieras y de las más grandes corporaciones. También lo es de la moda, la publicidad, los medios de comunicación y las artes. Washington, D.C. es la capital de la nación. El noreste ha sido la puerta de entrada principal de los inmigrantes. Millones de personas han pasado a través de Ellis Island en Nueva York y por otros centros de entrada de la región.

Hoy en día, los habitantes del sur de los Estados Unidos se ganan la vida de muchas maneras diferentes. El cultivo de productos y la cria de animales ha sido posible gracias a la riqueza de sus recursos naturales y un clima templado. El algodón ha sido una fuente importante de ingresos para los agricultores del sur, pero ya no es el único producto cultivado por la mayoría de ellos. La perforación petrolera, la minería, la pesca y el cuidado forestal también son industrias importantes en el sur de los Estados Unidos. El cambio de una economía basada en la agricultura a una economía basada en la industria, llamado industrialización, ha ocurrido durante los últimos 50 años. Hoy en día, industrias de texiles y de televisión por cable son muy comunes en la región. Sus puertos principales y su ubicación en el "cinturón soleado" del país, convierte a esta región en un lugar muy atractivo para los turistas. Washington, D.C., la capital de la nación, está ubicada en el sur.

Hasta la década de 1980, la mayoría del territorio del oeste medio estaba lleno de pequeñas granjas familiares. Sin embargo, durante los años ochenta, la recesión obligó a muchos de los agricultores a retirarse de esta industria. Las grandes corporaciones compraron la tierra y crearon grandes haciendas corporativas. La pérdida de tantos trabajos en el campo, obligó a millones de personas a buscar trabajo en zonas urbanas que incluyen Chicago, Detroit, San Luis y Minneapolis-St. Paul. Hoy en día, esos lugares son centros importantes para el transporte, la cultura, la manufactura, la banca y las publicaciones.

La principal atracción del oeste ha sido la enorme riqueza de sus recursos naturales. Aunque el oeste parecía como una zona de espacios abiertos infinitos, la población del oeste ha crecido tremendamente. La primera ola de crecimiento occurrió en 1849, cuando se descubrió oro en California y llegaron miles de mineros. Luego llegaron más pobladores. Durante muchos años, los habitantes simplemente usaban los recursos naturales que encontraban a su paso. Pero finalmente, el congreso creó bosques y parques nacionales para proteger algunas zonas del oeste. Hoy en día, las asociaciones de ciudadanos, la industria y el gobierno están trabajando juntos para lograr una mejor administración de los recursos del oeste y usarlos de manera inteligente.

CAPÍTULO
4

Exploremos los Estados Unidos

Instrucciones: A continuación hay una lista de términos del Capítulo 4. Escribe una oración o una frase en otra hoja de papel que describa el significado de cada término. Si es necesario, fíjate en el Capítulo 4 para que veas cómo se usan los términos.

1. viajes cotidianos—la rutina diaria de ir y volver del trabajo

_____

2. megalópolis—ciudades y centros urbanos que forman juntos una extensa zona urbana

_____

3. densidad de población—número promedio de personas por milla cuadrada o por kilómetro cuadrado

_____

4. industrialización—cambio de una economía basada en la agricultura a una basada en la industria

_____

5. hacienda de cultivos mixtos—una hacienda que produce diferentes tipos de cultivos

_____

6. recesión—disminución en la prosperidad económica; no tan severa como la depresión

_____

7. hacienda corporativa—gran hacienda administrada por una corporación

_____

8. *forty niners*—los primeros mineros que llegaron a California durante la fiebre del oro de 1849

_____

9. transporte masivo—sistema de transporte subterráneo, de buses y trenes, usado para transportar grandes cantidades de personas

_____

Spanish Support

CARTA PARA LA FAMILIA

CAPÍTULO 5

Exploremos el Canadá

La Línea Abierta de Ciencias Sociales

Querida familia:

En nuestra clase de ciencias sociales estamos llegando al final de nuestro estudio de los Estados Unidos y el Canadá. Durante los próximos días, estudiaremos en mayor detalle al Canadá, con un enfoque en las siguientes provincias o regiones: Ontario y Quebec, las llanuras canadienses, British Columbia, las provincias del Atlántico y los territorios del norte.

A medida que su hijo o hija lea acerca del Canadá en el Capítulo 5, podrían buscar juntos en un atlas las provincias y los territorios que estamos estudiando. Hágale preguntas como: "¿En qué se diferencian esas regiones? ¿Qué tipos de clima crees que podrían tener? ¿Cuál es la región más poblada?"

Converse con su hijo o hija acerca de la cultura francesa de la provincia de Quebec. Puede que él o ella haya escuchado noticias sobre la intención de los habitantes de esa provincia de separarse del Canadá para formar una nación independiente. Busque artículos que traten sobre ese conflicto y compártalos con su hijo o hija. Hablen acerca de cómo esa separación puede afectar a los habitantes del Canadá. Para que su hijo o hija comprenda mejor esos conceptos, podrán compararlos con eventos similares que hayan occurido en los Estados Unidos, como por ejemplo: la intención del sur de abandonar al norte durante la Guerra Civil, o el interés de algunos californianos de dividir el estado en dos o tres estados independientes.

A medida que su hijo o hija estudia las provincias de la pradera, usted podría hablarle de la manera en que se cultiva y se procesa el trigo para crear productos alimenticios. Conversen sobre la importancia del trigo, que es el principal cultivo de la región, y de cómo afecta la economía.

A su hijo o hija podría interesarle aprender más sobre cómo la ubicación de una comunidad puede afectar la cultura y la economía de sus habitantes. Por ejemplo: Vancouver, British Columbia, está ubicada en la costa del Pacífico y ha establecido vínculos muy fuertes con muchos países de Asia. ¿Cómo afecta a nuestra comunidad su ubicación?

Gracias por su ayuda mientras estudiamos a los Estados Unidos y al Canadá. Espero que usted haya disfrutado al compartir esta experiencia con su hijo o hija.

Atentamente,

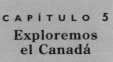

CAPÍTULO 5
Exploremos
el Canadá

Ontario y Quebec:
Conexión de dos culturas

A. Durante la lectura

Instrucciones: A medida que vayas leyendo la Sección 1, escribe tus respuestas a las siguientes preguntas en los espacios en blanco.

1. ¿Qué río forma la frontera entre Ontario y Quebec?

_____

2. ¿Cuáles son los principales idiomas que se hablan en Ontario y en Quebec?

_____

3. ¿Cómo fue que Toronto adquirió tanta diversidad en sus habitantes?

_____

4. ¿Por qué tantas personas en Quebec son de ascendencia francesa?

_____

5. ¿Cuál es el objetivo de los separatistas en Quebec?

_____

B. Repaso de los términos clave

Instrucciones: Para completar cada oración, escribe el término correspondiente en el espacio en blanco.

6. Muchos residentes de Quebec son _____, o sea, personas para quienes su primer idioma es el francés.

7. El movimiento _____ en Quebec trabajó para convertir al francés en el idioma oficial de la provincia.

8. Aunque el monarca británico es el jefe de estado canadiense, Canadá es un país que se gobierna por sí mismo, o sea es _____.

9. La rocosa y despoblada _____ se extiende desde la Bahía de Hudson hasta los Grandes Lagos.

10. Cuando en un país ocurren grandes cambios sin violencia, se le llama una _____.

11. Las 13 provincias y territorios del Canadá están unidas en una _____.

12. En _____ de 1980 y 1995, los habitantes de Quebec votaron para que Quebec siguiera siendo una parte del Canadá.

Spanish Support

Ontario y Quebec:
Conexión de dos culturas

A. Términos y conceptos clave

Instrucciones: Lee las oraciones a continuación. Si una oración es verdadera, escribe V en el espacio en blanco. Si es falsa, escribe F. En otra hoja de papel, vuelve a escribir las oraciones falsas en otra hoja de papel para convertirlas en verdaderas.

_____ **1.** La ciudad capital del Canadá es Toronto.

_____ **2.** La parte norteña de Ontario es parte del escudo canadiense.

_____ **3.** Montreal es la ciudad más grande de Quebec.

_____ **4.** Jacques Cartier desembarcó en Stadacona y declaró que la región pertenecía a Inglaterra

_____ **5.** En un plebiscito, los votantes votan a favor o en contra de un asunto.

B. Ideas principales

Instrucciones: En cada espacio en blanco, escribe la letra que mejor conteste la pregunta.

_____ **6.** El primer idioma de la mayoría de los habitantes de Québec es
    a. el inglés.   **c.** el español.
    b. el francés.   **d.** el italiano.

_____ **7.** La sede del gobierno canadiense se encuentra en la provincia de
    a. Quebec.   **c.** British Columbia.
    b. Montreal.   **d.** Ontario.

_____ **8.** ¿Cuál de estas cosas es verdad acerca de Toronto?
    a. Antes se le decía la Nueva Francia.
    b. Se encuentra en Quebec.
    c. Es la ciudad más grande del Canadá.
    d. Fue fundada en 1793 como Stadacona.

_____ **9.** ¿Cuál fue uno de los resultados de la Guerra Franco Indígena?
    a. Inglaterra capturó a Quebec.
    b. Todos los colonos franceses se fueron de América del Norte.
    c. Francia se apoderó de Montreal.
    d. Quebec se convirtió en la capital del Canadá.

_____ **10.** Una manera en que los habitantes de Quebec han podido conservar su cultura es
    a. separándose del resto del Canadá.   **c.** hablando sólo inglés.
    b. cambiando la constitución canadiense.   **d.** celebrando festivales.

CAPÍTULO 5
Exploremos el Canadá

Las llanuras canadienses
La despensa del Canadá

A. Durante la lectura

Instrucciones: A medida que vayas leyendo la Sección 2, completa la siguiente tabla con información sobre las llanuras canadienses.

La vida en las llanuras canadienses

Las provincias de la pradera	1.
	2.
Los pueblos nativos	3.
	4.
Los cambios en la forma de vida	5.
	6.
La tierra gratuita para los colonos	7.
	8.
Fomento de las tradiciones	9.
	10.

B. Repaso de los términos clave

Instrucciones: En el espacio en blanco a continuación, escribe la definición para los siguientes términos clave.

11. ascendencia

_____

12. inmunidad

_____

Las llanuras canadienses
La despensa del Canadá

A. Términos y conceptos clave

Instrucciones: Empareja las definiciones de la Columna I con los términos de la Columna II. Escribe la letra correspondiente en cada espacio en blanco.

Columna I

_____ 1. Alguien que haya sido expuesto a una enfermedad tiene ____, o resistencia natural a esa enfermedad.

_____ 2. A las llanuras canadienses a veces les llaman ____ por los muchos cultivos de trigo que hay allí.

_____ 3. Los primeros inmigrantes a la región fueron de ____ europea.

_____ 4. La ciudad de ____, en Alberta, celebra la ganadería con un rodeo anual.

_____ 5. El sitio en Saskatchewan que el pueblo cree una vez llamó Oscana es ____.

Columna II

a. la despensa del Canadá

b. ascendencia

c. inmunidad

d. Regina

e. Calgary

B. Ideas principales

Instrucciones: En cada espacio en blanco, escribe la letra que mejor conteste la pregunta.

_____ 6. ¿Cuál fue una manera en que los colonos europeos cambiaron las culturas de los pueblos nativos en las provincias de la pradera?
　　a. Insistieron en que se vistieran con ropa europea.
　　b. Trajeron enfermedades contra las cuales los indígenas no tenían ninguna resistencia.
　　c. Les pidieron que hablaran francés.
　　d. Establecieron escuelas.

_____ 7. ¿Por qué llegó a su fin la forma de vivir de tantos pueblos nativos en la región de las llanuras de América del Norte a fines de la década de 1870?
　　a. Los europeos trajeron caballos a América del Norte para reemplazar a búfalo.
　　b. Los pueblos nativos se mudaron a las grandes ciudades industriales.
　　c. Los europeos comenzar a acabar con las manadas de búfalos.
　　d. Los pueblos nativos se fueron de América del Norte a Europa.

_____ 8. Después de que el gobierno canadiense ofreciera terrenos gratuitos en los periódicos europeos,
　　a. muchas personas se mudaron a los Estados Unidos.
　　b. muchas personas se fueron del Canadá.
　　c. los pueblos nativos obtuvieron nuevos terrenos.
　　d. disminuyó la inmigración.

_____ 9. La mayoría de los inmigrantes europeos que fueron a las provincias de la pradera se hicieron
　　a. banqueros.
　　b. comerciantes.
　　c. educadores.
　　d. agricultores.

_____ 10. La Estampida de Calgary celebra ____ de la región.
　　a. la cosecha de trigo
　　b. el legado del comercio de pieles
　　c. el legado del bailes
　　d. el legado de la ganadería

CAPÍTULO 5
Exploremos el Canadá

British Columbia: Vínculos con las naciones de la costa del Pacífico

3

A. Durante la lectura

Instrucciones: A medida que vayas leyendo la Sección 3, completa las siguientes oraciones.

1. Cada uno de los primeros grupos que llegaron a la British Columbia tenía una sociedad compleja y sus propias _____ .

2. Los primeros exploradores europeos que llegaron a finales del siglo XVI, tenían el propósito de _____ .

3. La vida de los pueblos nativos en la British Columbia no cambió tanto a causa del comercio con los europeos como a causa del descubrimiento de _____ .

4. La población de Victoria se duplicó de un día para otro con la llegada de 450 _____ .

5. La razón por la que a las _____ les fue tan bien en la región del caribú fue porque el gobierno construyó una carretera allí.

6. A finales del siglo XIX, las leyes canadienses prohibieron _____ , _____ , y _____ de los nativos americanos.

7. Hoy en día, los pueblos nativos están demandando terrenos y _____ políticos.

8. En 1881, los canadienses comenzaron a trabajar en un _____ que uniría a Vancouver y Montreal.

9. Muchos de los habitantes de la British Columbia de hoy en día piensan que su futuro depende de _____ más que del Canadá.

10. El cuarenta por ciento del comercio de la British Columbia es con países de _____ .

B. Repaso de los términos clave

Instrucciones: Escribe el término clave correspondiente para cada una de las siguientes definiciones.

11. palo grande de madera tallado con símbolos del grupo, clan o familia de los pueblos nativos

_____

12. pueblo o ciudad que crece rápidamente para suplir las necesidades de los mineros

_____

Spanish Support

3

British Columbia: Vínculos con las naciones de la costa del Pacífico

A. Términos y conceptos clave

Instrucciones: Empareja las definiciones de la Columna I con los términos de la Columna II. Escribe la letra correspondiente en cada espacio en blanco.

Columna I

_____ **1.** objeto tallado con símbolos de un grupo, clan o familia

_____ **2.** pueblo diseñado para suplir las necesidades de los mineros

_____ **3.** pequeño pueblo comercial establecido por los británicos en la Isla de Vancouver

_____ **4.** lugar en el que los mineros descubrieron oro

_____ **5.** terreno que bordea al Océano Pacífico

Columna II

a. colonia próspera

b. Victoria

c. las naciones de la costa del Pacífico

d. los Montes Caribú

e. tótem

B. Ideas principales

Instrucciones: En cada espacio en blanco, escribe la letra que mejor conteste la pregunta.

_____ **6.** Los exploradores europeos llegaron por primera vez a lo que hoy en día es British Columbia con el objetivo de
    a. cultivar.
    b. comerciar.
    c. construir escuelas.
    d. establecer colonias.

_____ **7.** En 1858, ¿qué evento importante cambió la vida en la Isla de Vancouver?
    a. Los pueblos nativos fueron contagiados por la sarampión traida por los colonos europeos.
    b. Los españoles llegaron a la isla.
    c. Los británicos construyeron un lugar para el comercio de pieles.
    d. Alguien descubrió oro a lo largo del Río Fraser.

_____ **8.** En 1888, ¿cómo decidió el gobierno británico cambiar la vida de los pueblos nativos de la British Columbia?
    a. Los obligó a vivir en pequeñas reservas.
    b. Los obligó a emigrar a Francia.
    c. Los obligó a emigrar a los Estados Unidos.
    d. Los obligó a vender sus tierras.

_____ **9.** El objetivo de construir un ferrocarril de Montreal a Vancouver era para
    a. atraer a los colonos europeos a Montreal.
    b. unir al Canadá con los Estados Unidos.
    c. unificar al Canadá.
    d. llevar a los pueblos nativos a un nuevo territorio.

_____ **10.** El comercio, la diversidad de habitantes y la geografía física une a la provincia de la British Columbia con
    a. las naciones de la costa del Pacífico.
    b. los Estados Unidos.
    c. Europa.
    d. la Gran Bretaña.

CAPÍTULO 5
Exploremos
el Canadá

Las provincias del Atlántico
Unidas por los mares

A. Durante la lectura

Instrucciones: A medida que vayas leyendo la Sección 4, escribe tus respuestas a las siguientes preguntas en los espacios en blanco.

1. ¿Cuáles son las provincias del Atlántico?

_____

2. ¿Cómo afecta la geografía de las provincias del Atlántico la manera de vivir de sus residentes?

_____

3. ¿Por qué se exilaron de Acadia las personas de ascendencia francesa?

_____

4. ¿Cuál es el enfoque de la economía en las provincias del Atlántico?

_____

5. ¿Cómo cambió la industria de la construcción de buques (los astilleros) durante la década de 1880?

_____

6. ¿Qué tan importante es la pesca hoy día en las provincias del Atlántico?

_____

7. ¿Cómo afectó la prohibición de la pesca del bacalao en 1992 la industria pesquera de Terranova?

_____

8. ¿Qué industrias nuevas han surgido en las provincias del Atlántico?

_____

B. Repaso de los términos clave

Instrucciones: Para completar cada oración, escribe el término correspondiente en el espacio en blanco.

9. A los residentes de Acadia de ascendencia francesa los _____, o sea, los obligaron a irse de la región.

10. Una industria _____ es una relacionada con la navegación o el comercio por el mar.

11. En Nueva Brunswick, los residentes se dedican a la _____ , o sea al cultivo de peces en granjas.

Spanish Support

EXAMEN DE LA SECCIÓN

Las provincias del Atlántico
Unidas por los mares

A. Términos y conceptos clave

Instrucciones: Lee las oraciones a continuación. Si una oración es verdadera, escribe V en el espacio en blanco. Si es falsa, escribe F. En otra hoja de papel, vuelve a escribir las oraciones falsas en otra hoja de papel para convertirlas en verdaderas.

_____ **1.** Se cree que L'Anse aux Meadows es un sitio donde se asentaron los vikingos.

_____ **2.** La industria de la acuacultura incluye el cultivo de peces.

_____ **3.** La banca es un ejemplo de una industria marítima.

_____ **4.** Acadia fue el primer asentamiento francés en América del Norte.

_____ **5.** Una persona que ha sido exilada de un sitio puede regresar a visitarla cuando quiera.

B. Ideas principales

Instrucciones: En cada espacio en blanco, escribe la letra que mejor conteste la pregunta.

_____ **6.** ¿Cuál de las siguientes no es una provincia del Atlántico?
    a. Nueva Brunswick   **c.** Terranova
    b. Prince Edward Island   **d.** Quebec

_____ **7.** ¿Cuáles dos países se pelearon por controlar la zona oriental del Canadá?
    a. Estados Unidos y el Canadá   **c.** Francia e Italia
    b. Francia e Inglaterra   **d.** Alemania e Inglaterra

_____ **8.** Una industria que ha sido muy importante para la economía de esta región es
    a. la construcción.   **c.** la pesca.
    b. el cultivo de trigo.   **d.** la siderurgia.

_____ **9.** ¿A qué factor se debió la desaceleración de la economía de la región en la década de 1880?
    a. Más y más buques se hicieron de madera en lugar de acero.
    b. Más y más buques se hicieron de acero en lugar de madera.
    c. Se prohibió la pesca de bacalao.
    d. El procesamiento de pescados produjó muchas ganancias.

_____ **10.** Una manera en que se está tratando de ampliar las industrias en la región es con
    a. el cultivo de mejillones.   **c.** el cultivo de maíz.
    b. la construcción de rascacielos.   **d.** el procesamiento de carne de cerdo.

CAPÍTULO 5
Exploremos
el Canadá

Los territorios del norte
Nuevas fronteras

A. Durante la lectura

Instrucciones: A medida que vayas leyendo la Sección 5, completa la siguiente tabla con información sobre los territorios del norte.

Geografía	1.
	2.
Población	3.
	4.
Gobierno	5.
	6.
La fiebre del oro	7.
	8.
Nunavut	9.
	10.

B. Repaso de los términos clave

Instrucciones: En el espacio en blanco a continuación, escribe la definición para el siguiente término clave.

11. aurora boreal

_____

Nombre_____ Clase_____ Fecha_____

Los territorios del norte
Nuevas fronteras

A. Términos y conceptos clave

Instrucciones: Empareja las definiciones de la Columna I con los términos de la Columna II. Escribe la letra correspondiente en cada espacio en blanco.

Columna I

_____ **1.** La capital de Nunavut es _____

_____ **2.** En el territorio del _____ se realizó la famosa fiebre del oro del Klondike en 1896.

_____ **3.** _____ significa 'nuestro territorio' en el idioma inuit de los inuktitut.

_____ **4.** Los territorios del norte son sitios excelentes para ver el espectáculo de luz natural llamado _____.

_____ **5.** La población del pueblo de _____, cayó de unos 30,000 a unos 1,300 después de que se calmó la fiebre del oro.

Columna II

a. Yukon

b. aurora boreal

c. Iqaluit

d. Nunavut

e. Dawson

B. Ideas principales

Instrucciones: En cada espacio en blanco, escribe la letra que mejor conteste la pregunta.

6. ¿Por qué hay tan pocos habitantes en los territorios del norte?
  a. Es ilegal vivir allí.
  b. La zona es más que todo tundra.
  c. El clima es demasiado caliente.
  d. Las luces norteñas son peligrosas.

7. Casi la mitad de las personas que viven en los Territorios del Noroeste son
  a. pueblos nativos.
  b. visitantes.
  c. de los Estados Unidos.
  d. inmigrantes chinos.

8. ¿Cuál es una manera en que los gobiernos de los territorios del norte es distinto de los gobiernos de las provincias canadienses?
  a. Los territorios no están representados en el Parlamento.
  b. Los territorios no tienen cuerpos legislativos.
  c. Los territorios tienen más poder para imponer impuestos.
  d. El gobierno federal tiene más control sobre los territorios.

9. ¿Por qué se llamó en una época a Dawson la "París del norte"?
  a. Allí se asentaron muchos pobladores franceses.
  b. Allí sólo se hablaba francés.
  c. Muchos residentes de Dawson habían ido a París.
  d. Tenía muchos teatros y salones de baile para entretener a los mineros de oro.

10. ¿Cuál es un reto que enfrentan hoy los residentes de Nunavut?
  a. convertirse en territorio canadiense
  b. encontrar oro
  c. mantener la economía fuerte
  d. prohibir los teléfonos celulares

CAPÍTULO
5

Exploremos el Canadá

Preguntas guía:

- ¿Cómo han afectado los acontecimientos históricos las culturas de los Estados Unidos y el Canadá?
- ¿Cómo ha beneficiado y desafiado a los dos países la variedad de los habitantes de los Estados Unidos y el Canadá?

<u>Canadá es un país de muchas culturas.</u> Al Canadá han emigrado personas de todas las partes del mundo. Aunque cada una de las 13 provincias y territorios tiene una historia y una cultura diferentes, todas están unidas en una federación.

<u>Ontario y Quebec son las dos provincias más pobladas, pero estas provincias tienen legados culturales muy diferentes.</u> Ontario incluye a Ottawa, la capital del Canadá, y a la ciudad más grande del Canadá, Toronto. Toronto tiene una población muy diversa. Los primeros pobladores de Quebec fueron los colonos franceses. El francés es el idioma oficial de Quebec. Incluso hoy, los francófonos (o sea las personas que hablan francés) son la mayoría en Quebec. Muchas de esas personas piensan que Quebec debe ser un país independiente. En 1995, apenas se derrotó un voto que buscaba la separación de la provincia del Canadá.

<u>Las provincias de la pradera es encuentran en la pradera más extensa del mundo. Se les dice el granero del Canadá debido a que allí se produce tanto trigo.</u> Los inmigrantes llegaron a las provincias de la pradera cuando el gobierno canadiense publicitó terrenos gratuitos. Llevaron una vida muy ardua pero con el tiempo triunfaron y crearon una región agrícola productiva. Pero los nuevos granjeros afectaron de manera negativa la forma de vivir de los pueblos nativos. Los nuevos pobladores mataron muchos búfalos y los europeos llegaron con enfermedades para las cuales los pueblos nativos no tenían ninguna inmunidad.

<u>La provincia de British Columbia tiene una población muy diversa.</u> La primera gran ola de personas llegó cuando se descubrió el oro. Los mineros transformaron la vida de todos. Los pueblos nativos fueron desplazados de sus tierras y pasados a reservas. En 1881, se comenzó la construcción del Ferrocarril del Pacífico Canadiense, que comunicó a British Columbia con el resto del Canadá. Pero debido a la ubicación de la provincia al lado del Océano Pacífico, muchos habitantes de British Columbia piensan que sus nexos son más fuertes con los países de la zona del Pacífico.

<u>En las provincias del Atlántico, que se encuentran a lo largo del Océano Atlántico, la forma de vivir está muy vinculada con el mar.</u> Las personas de ascendencia francesa fueron exiladas cuando los británicos se apoderaron de Acadia en 1763. La mayoría de los habitantes viven en la costa y la pesca siempre ha desempeñado un papel importante en la economía. A medida que la pesca ha cambiado, los residentes han modificado su forma de vivir, explorando industrias tales como el procesamiento de pescado y la acuacultura.

<u>Los territorios del norte están escasamente poblados y muchos de sus residentes son indígenas.</u> Los tres territorios son los Territorios del Noroeste, el Yukón y Nunavut, que se formó cuando el pueblo inuit peticionó al gobierno canadiense para obtener su territorio propio. Los terrenos son accidentados y el clima es muy frío. El gobierno federal tiene un poco más de control sobre los territorios que sobre las provincias, aunque cada territorio tiene su propio cuerpo legislativo.

Spanish Support

Nombre _____ Clase _____ Fecha _____

Exploremos el Canadá

Instrucciones: Empareja los términos clave de la tabla con las definiciones de abajo. Escribe la letra correspondiente en cada espacio en blanco. Luego escribe una oración que use el término o la forma plural del término en el espacio respectivo. Si es necesario, observa los términos en el glosario de tu libro de texto o fíjate cómo se usan en el Capítulo 5.

a. colonia próspera	**d.** revolución pacífica	**g.** tótem
b. francoparlante	**e.** plebiscito	**h.** marítimo
c. inmunidad	**f.** separatista	**i.** aurora boreal

_____ **1.** voto en el cual las personas deciden si están a favor o en contra de algo específico

_____

_____

_____ **2.** Espectáculo de luz natural que se ve en el Hemisferio Norte

_____

_____

_____ **3.** cambio sin violencia en el gobierno de la provincia de Quebec en 1976

_____

_____

_____ **4.** en el Canadá, alguien que quiere que la provincia de Quebec se separe del resto del país

_____

_____

_____ **5.** palo grande de madera tallada con símbolos del grupo, clan o familia de pueblos nativos

_____

_____ **6.** persona que habla francés como su primera lengua

_____

_____ **7.** pueblo o ciudad que crece rápidamente y disfruta de bonanza, generalmente para suplir las necesidades de los mineros

_____

_____ **8.** se relaciona con la navegación o el comercio por el mar

_____

_____ **9.** resistencia natural a las enfermedades

_____

Glosario

A

abolitionist
abolicionista persona que creía que la esclavitud era equivocada y que quería terminar esta práctica

acid rain
lluvia ácida lluvia con un alto contenido de sustancias químicas que contamina y deteriora el medio ambiente; por lo general es causada por el uso excesivo de combustibles

agribusiness
empresa agrícola compañía grande que maneja enormes haciendas para producir, procesar y distribuir productos agrícolas; compañía que manufactura y distribuye maquinaria y herramientas agrícolas

alluvial
aluvial depósito arcilloso que queda en la capa superior del suelo después de una inundación

aquaculture
acuacultura el cultivo de peces y plantas acuáticas

aurora borealis
aurora boreal bandas de luz de gran colorido que pueden ser vistas en los cielos del Norte

autonomous
autónomo que se gobierna por sí solo

B

bilingual
bilingüe alguien que habla dos idiomas; que tiene dos idiomas oficiales

boomtown
colonia próspera pueblo o ciudad que crece rápidamente y disfruta de bonanza, generalmente para suplir las necesidades de los mineros

boycott
boicot rehusar a comprar o a usar ciertos productos o servicios

C

civil rights movement
movimiento por los derechos civiles numeroso grupo de personas que se unieron, a principios de los años sesenta, para terminar con la segregación de los afroamericanos y para apoyar la igualdad de derechos de todas las minorías

Civil War
Guerra Civil guerra entre los estados del norte y los estados del sur de los Estados Unidos que empezó en 1861 y terminó en 1865

Spanish Support

Glosario

clear-cutting
despeje forestal tipo de explotación de bosques en la que se cortan todos los árboles de una zona

Cold War
Guerra Fría período de tensión entre los Estados Unidos y la Unión Soviética en el que, a pesar de su nombre, no hubo guerra convencional; duró desde 1945 hasta 1990

communism
comunismo sistema de gobierno en el que el estado posee y controla todas las empresas e industrias

commute
viajes cotidianos la rutina de ir y volver del trabajo

Continental Divide
divisoria continental límite que separa los ríos que fluyen hacia lados opuestos de un continente; en América del Norte, las Montañas Rocosas

corporate farm
hacienda corporativa gran hacienda administrada por una corporación; puede estar formada por pequeñas haciendas que antes pertenecían a familias

cultural diversity
diversidad cultural gran variedad de culturas

cultural exchange
intercambio cultural proceso en el que diferentes culturas comparten ideas y formas de hacer las cosas

D

descent
ascendencia linaje

dominion
dominio región que tiene un gobierno propio, pero que depende de la Gran Bretaña; por ejemplo, el Canadá y Australia antes de 1939

E

ethnic group
grupo étnico grupo de personas que pueden tener en común un mismo lenguaje, religión y tradiciones culturales

exile
exilar expulsión obligatoria de cierta región

Glosario

F

federation
federación una unión de estados, grupos, provincias o países

forty-niner
forty niner los primeros mineros que llegaron a California durante la fiebre del oro de 1849

fossil fuel
combustible fósil recurso mineral formado durante millones de años por los restos de plantas y animales; por ejemplo: el carbón, la gasolina y el gas natural

Francophone
francoparlante persona que habla francés como su primera lengua

free trade
libre comercio mercado sin tarifas sobre los productos importados

G

geographic diversity
diversidad geográfica variedad de accidentes geográficos, clima y vegetación

glacier
glaciar gran masa de hielo que se mueve lentamente sobre la tierra, formada a lo largo de mucho tiempo por capas de nieve bajo presión que se no se descongelan

H

Homestead Act
Acta de Residencia ley aprobada en 1862 en la que se otorgaban 160 acres (65 hectáreas) de tierra en las llanuras del oeste medio de los Estados Unidos a cualquier adulto dispuesto a vivir y trabajar en ella por cinco años

hydroelectricity
hidroelectricidad electricidad producida por torrentes de agua

I

immigrant
inmigrante persona que llega a un país, procedente de otro, con la intención de residir allí

immunity
inmunidad resistencia natural a alguna enfermedad

indentured servant
siervo por contrato persona que, a cambio de los beneficios recibidos, debe trabajar por algunos años para obtener su libertad

Spanish Support

Glosario

indigenous
nativos originarios de un lugar en particular

industrialization
industrialización cambio de una economía basada en la agricultura a una basada en la industria; el desarrollo de grandes industrias

Industrial Revolution
revolución industrial período de transición de la elaboración de productos a mano, a la elaboración de productos con la ayuda de maquinaria

interdependent
interdependiente dependiente el uno del otro

L

labor force
fuerza laboral la oferta o disponibilidad de trabajadores

Louisiana Purchase
La Compra de Luisiana la venta de tierras que hizo Francia a Estados Unidos en 1803; todas las tierras entre el Río Misisipí y la ladera oriental de las Montañas Rocosas

M

Manifest Destiny
destino manifiesto la creencia de que los Estados Unidos tenía el derecho a poseer y gobernar toda la tierra entre el Atlántico y el Pacífico de América del Norte

maritime
marítimo relacionado con la navegación o el comercio por el mar

mass transit
transporte masivo sistema de transporte subterráneo, de buses y trenes, usado para transportar grandes cantidades de personas

megalopolis
megalópolis ciudades y centros urbanos que forman juntos una extensa zona urbana

missionary
misionero persona que trataba de convertir a otros a su religión, y que a veces ofrecía servicios de salud y educación

mixed-crop farm
hacienda de cultivos mixtos una hacienda que produce diferentes tipos de cultivos

Glosario

N

NAFTA
NAFTA Tratado de Libre Comercio, firmado en 1994 entre el Canadá, los Estados Unidos y México, para establecer un acuerdo de libre comercio mutuo

P

permafrost
permafrost capa de tierra permanentemente congelada

petrochemical
petroquímico sustancia hecha a base de petróleo, como el plástico, la pintura o el asfalto

plantation
plantación hacienda grande con muchos trabajadores donde se cultiva un solo producto; las plantaciones eran comunes en las colonias del sur de los Estados Unidos

population density
densidad de población número promedio de personas por milla cuadra o por kilómetro cuadrado

prairie
pradera región de terrenos planos cubiertos de pastos altos; llanura

province
provincia división política de tierra en el Canadá, similar a un estado de los Estados Unidos

Q

Quiet Revolution
revolución pacífica cambio en el gobierno de la provincia de Quebec en el que el Partido Quebequés (*Parti Québécois*) tomó el control de la legislatura e impuso el francés como idioma oficial

R

rain shadow
sombra de lluvia región en el lado protegido de una montaña que recibe muy poca lluvia

recession
recesión disminución en la prosperidad económica; no tan severa como la depresión

Reconstruction
reconstrucción plan para reedificar después de la Guerra Civil de los Estados Unidos; incluye el período en que el sur del país fue gobernado por el ejército de los Estados Unidos

Spanish Support

Glosario

referendum
plebiscito voto en el cual las personas deciden si están a favor o en contra de un tema específico

reserve
reserva zonas separadas por el gobierno canadiense para los pueblos nativos

Revolutionary War
la guerra de la independencia guerra entre 1775 y 1781, en la que las colonias americanas obtuvieron su independencia de Inglaterra

S

segregate
segregar separar o apartar

separatist
separatista en el Canadá, alguien que quiere que la provincia de Quebec se separe del resto del país

settlement house
residencia comunitaria centro comunitario en los Estados Unidos para inmigrantes pobres; por ejemplo, la residencia comunitaria Jane Addams Hull House en Chicago

Sun Belt
cinturón soleado área de los Estados Unidos que va desde la costa sur del Atlántico a la costa de California; conocida por su clima cálido

T

tariff
tarifa derechos que cobra el gobierno por mercancía importada

totem pole
tótem palo grande de madera tallada con símbolos de una tribu, clan o familia; tradicional de los nativos del noroeste de América del Norte

tributary
tributario río o corriente de agua que desemboca en un río principal

tropics
trópicos áreas del planeta entre las líneas de latitud $23\frac{1}{2}°$N y $23\frac{1}{2}°$S, donde el clima es casi siempre cálido

tundra
tundra región seca y fría cubierta de hielo por más de la mitad del año; vasta región plana y sin árboles, donde el subsuelo permanece congelado aún en el verano

Respuestas

Capítulo 1

Sección 1 Lectura dirigida y repaso

1. en Norte América
2. El Canadá; los Estados Unidos
3. las Montañas Rocosas y los Apalaches/la meseta de San Lorenzo; una región enorme de llanuras que se conoce en el Canadá como la Llanura Interior, y en los Estados Unidos como las Grandes Llanuras o la Llanura Central
4. la Sierra Nevada y las Cascadas
5. al este de la Llanura Interior; porque el terreno es muy rocoso y escarpado
6. en las tierras bajas de San Lorenzo; porque la región es el centro de manufactura del Canadá y la tierra es muy fértil y buena para la agricultura
7. de glaciares; durante un período glaciar hace miles de años
8. el Río Mackenzie y el Río San Lorenzo
9. porque es una de las rutas de transporte más usadas en América del Norte; conecta a los Grandes Lagos con el Océano Atlántico
10. tributario
11. glaciares
12. divisoria continental

Sección 1 Examen

1. e
2. a
3. d
4. b
5. c
6. c
7. a
8. b
9. b
10. d

Sección 2 Lectura dirigida y repaso

Las oraciones pueden variar. Damos ejemplos de respuestas.

1. Por lo general, el clima es frío debido a la latitud tan al norte; en el oeste, la influencia del océano crea un clima marino moderado; en las llanuras del interior hace mucho frío en el invierno y calor en el verano; la región del oeste es seca debido a la sombra de lluvia creada por las Montañas Rocosas.
2. Hay mucha variedad en clima, desde el frío de Alaska en el norte hasta el calor de Florida y Hawai en el sur; hay desiertos cálidos al oeste de la Sierra Nevada; en las Grandes Llanuras hace frío en el invierno y calor en el verano; la región del este tiene climas continentales; en el norte del país, los inviernos son fríos con nieve y los veranos son cálidos; en el sur del país, los veranos son largos y cálidos, y los inviernos son templados.
3. muy al norte; frío, seco y cubierto de nieve por lo menos la mitad del año; musgos, pastos y flores silvestres crecen solamente en el verano; permafrost
4. praderas cubiertas de pastos altos en las llanuras de los Estados Unidos y el Canadá; pastos más bajos en las Grandes Llanuras debido a que hay menos lluvia; el trigo crece bien
5. la Gran Cuenca entre las Montañas Rocosas y la Sierra Nevada en los Estados Unidos; región de pastos bajos y arbustos
6. cerca de un tercio de los Estados Unidos y cerca de la mitad del Canadá; árboles coníferos en el norte de la Costa del Pacífico, las Montañas Rocosas y los Apalaches; árboles coníferos mezclados con árboles deciduos desde los Grandes Lagos hasta el sureste del Canadá y Nueva Inglaterra y hasta el sureste de los Estados Unidos
7. sombra de lluvia
8. permafrost
9. pradera
10. provincia

Sección 2 Examen

1. F; La sombra de lluvia es una región seca en el lado protegido de una montaña que recibe poca lluvia.
2. V
3. F; La tundra es una región seca y fría que está cubierta de nieve durante más de seis meses al año.
4. V
5. F; Una provincia es una división política del Canadá.
6. a

Respuestas

7. a
8. c
9. b
10. c

Sección 3 Lectura dirigida y repaso

1. tierra fértil
2. familias
3. Ejemplos de respuestas: para beber, para la agricultura, la manufactura, y el transporte y la generación de energía
4. carbón, petróleo y gas natural
5. la agricultura
6. riqueza mineral
7. provincias de las praderas
8. productos de madera
9. compuesto de materiales depositados en inundaciones
10. energía eléctrica generada por torrentes de agua
11. compañía grande que maneja enormes haciendas

Sección 3 Examen

1. b	6. b
2. e	7. b
3. d	8. c
4. a	9. d
5. c	10. a

Actividad de vocabulario

Las oraciones pueden variar. Damos ejemplos de respuestas.

1. Cuando los antiguos glaciares se descongelaron, llenaron depresiones profundas que llegaron a ser los Grandes Lagos.
2. Un tributario es un río o corriente que desemboca en un río más grande.
3. La frontera montañosa que separa los ríos que fluyen a los lados opuestos de un continente se llama divisoria continental.
4. La sombra de lluvia es una zona en el lado de una montaña donde la lluvia rara vez llega.
5. Las zonas entre las líneas de latitud $23\frac{1}{2}°$ N y $23\frac{1}{2}°$ S se llaman trópicos.
6. La tundra en el extremo norte del Canadá es un pésimo lugar para cultivar.
7. Durante el verano, la capa superior del permafrost se descongela.
8. Hallarás llanuras en las zonas que tienen un clima húmedo.
9. Una provincia canadiense es similar a un estado de los Estados Unidos.
10. La tierra fértil del aluvial es depositada por ríos.
11. Las empresas agrícolas son enormes granjas administradas por grandes compañías.
12. La hidroelectricidad puede ser generada por represas construidas sobre ríos.

Capítulo 2

Sección 1 Lectura dirigida y repaso

Las oraciones pueden variar. Damos ejemplos de respuestas.

1. Hace unos 30,000 años, grupos de personas emigraron de Asia; llegaron a habitar todo el continente americano; entre los grupos de nativos americanos había muchas culturas distintas.
2. Después de 1492, la forma de vida de muchos nativos americanos cambió; los colonizadores y los misioneros españoles los trataron mal; mercaderes franceses a menudo vivían con los nativos americanos y les quitaban sus tierras.
3. Los colonizadores ingleses establecieron 13 colonias a lo largo de la costa Atlántica; usaron esclavos africanos para trabajar en las plantaciones en el sur de los Estados Unidos; muchas colonias fueron establecidas por gente en busca de libertad religiosa; los colonizadores ayudaron a la Gran Bretaña a ganar la guerra contra los frances y los nativos americanos.
4. Las colonias pagaban impuestos a la Gran Bretaña; los colonizadores se opusieron y reclamaron representación en el gobierno británico; ese conflicto resultó en la guerra de la independencia; los colonizadores ganaron su independencia en 1781; los líderes de la revolución se reunieron y escribieron la Constitución, que estableció la base del gobierno de los Estados Unidos.
5. nativos

Respuestas

6. misioneros
7. siervo por contrato
8. plantación
9. boicot
10. la guerra de la independencia

Sección I Examen

1. c	6. b
2. e	7. b
3. a	8. c
4. b	9. d
5. d	10. b

Sección 2 Lectura dirigida y repaso

Las oraciones pueden variar. Damos ejemplos de respuestas.

1. Con La Compra de Luisiana, se dobló el tamaño de los Estados Unidos; los nativos americanos fueron expulsados de sus tierras; la región del suroeste se convirtió en territorio de los Estados Unidos.
2. Muchas personas, incluyendo muchos inmigrantes, fueron a las ciudades para trabajar en las fábricas; la revolución industrial ayudó a crear nuevos trabajos.
3. Debido a la desmotadora, el algodón llegó a ser un cultivo más lucrativo; los dueños de las plantaciones sureñas querían llevar la esclavitud a los nuevos estados del oeste; los abolicionistas del norte se opusieron; el conflicto se convirtió en una guerra.
4. El norte tenía más recursos, pero el Sur tenía el mejor ejército; la Guerra Civil duró cuatro años; el norte ganó en 1865; después de la guerra empezó la reconstrucción, un período en el que la nación intentó reedificarse; continuaron los conflictos sobre como gobernar al sur.
5. la compra de los Estados Unidos a Francia por todo el terreno entre el Río Misisipí y las laderas al este de las Montañas Rocosas
6. la creencia de que era el destino de los Estados Unidos poseer todo el territorio entre el Océano Atlántico y el Océano Pacífico
7. persona que llega a un país procedente de otro con la intención de residir allí

8. la transición de la elaboración de productos a mano a la elaboración de productos por maquinaria
9. persona que quería terminar la práctica de la esclavitud
10. la guerra entre los estados del norte y los estados del sur (1861–1865)
11. el plan para reedificar la nación después de la Guerra Civil
12. el acto de separar; en el sur, la intención de apartar a las personas de raza negra de las personas de raza blanca

Sección 2 Examen

1. c	6. b
2. a	7. b
3. e	8. c
4. b	9. d
5. d	10. b

Sección 3 Lectura dirigida y repaso

1. La mayoría permaneció pobre, viviendo en comunidades pobres superpobladas, y trabajando en fábricas.
2. Los Estados Unidos adquirió Alaska, Hawaii, Puerto Rico, las Filipinas y Guam, y tenía un estamento militar y una economía fuertes.
3. Alemania empezó a hundir barcos de los Estados Unidos.
4. Empezó la gran depresión; las fábricas cerraron; muchos perdieron sus trabajos y viviendas; algunos granjeros perdieron sus granjas.
5. la guerra de Korea y la guerra de Vietnam
6. Las respuestas variarán, pero pueden incluir el problema de las personas sin viviendas, el hambre, los sueldos bajos y la contaminación.
7. fuerza laboral
8. residencia comunitaria
9. Acta de Residencia
10. comunismo
11. Guerra Fría
12. movimiento por los derechos civiles

Sección 3 Examen

1. V
2. F; Bajo el comunismo, el estado es dueño de toda la industria.

Respuestas

3. V
4. F; Después de la Segunda Guerra Mundial, se inició la Guerra Fría entre los Estados Unidos y la Unión Soviética.
5. V
6. b
7. c
8. b
9. d
10. b

Sección 4 Lectura dirigida y repaso

1. rivales
2. Acta de Quebec
3. Alto, Bajo
4. Ontario, Quebec
5. guerra
6. crecimiento y cambio
7. súbditos británicos
8. Europa
9. respetar
10. independiente
11. bilingüe
12. dominio

Sección 4 Examen

1. c
2. a
3. b
4. e
5. d
6. a
7. b
8. d
9. c
10. a

Sección 5 Lectura dirigida y repaso

Las oraciones pueden variar. Damos ejemplos de respuestas.

1. Tanto los Estados Unidos como el Canadá dependen de la tecnología, pero el uso de ciertas tecnologías ha puesto en peligro algunos recursos naturales que ambos países comparten.
2. Los Estados Unidos y el Canadá han trabajado juntos para controlar la contaminación del agua y el aire.
3. Los Estados Unidos y el Canadá trabajan juntos para conservar los bosques y mantener la industria forastera.
4. Tanto los Estados Unidos como el Canadá se han beneficiado de la cooperación económica. Un ejemplo de esta cooperación es la construcción de la ruta marítima del Río San Lorenzo.
5. El Canadá es el principal socio comercial de los Estados Unidos y vice versa.
6. un combustible, como el carbón o el petróleo, formado de los restos de plantas y animales
7. lluvia con un alto contenido de ácido, formada por una mezcla de humedad y contaminantes
8. tipo de explotación forestal en la que se cortan todos los árboles de una zona dada
9. dependiente el uno del otro
10. derechos cobrados por mercancía importada
11. intercambio de mercancía sin restricciones o tarifas entre dos o más países
12. Tratado de Libre Comercio en el que los Estados Unidos, el Canadá y México llegaron a un acuerdo para mantener el libre comercio.

Sección 5 Examen

1. c
2. e
3. a
4. b
5. d
6. c
7. a
8. d
9. d
10. c

Actividad de vocabulario

1. c
2. j
3. l
4. d
5. f
6. a
7. i
8. e
9. s
10. k
11. g
12. m
13. q
14. r
15. o

Capítulo 3

Sección 1 Lectura dirigida y repaso

1. medio ambiente
2. caballos
3. trigo
4. cultura original, cambiar
5. países natales
6. identidad

Respuestas

7. diversidad
8. artistas
9. arte
10. intercambio cultural
11. grupo étnico
12. diversidad cultural

Sección I Examen

1. c		6. b	
2. e		7. b	
3. a		8. c	
4. b		9. d	
5. d		10. b	

Sección 2 Lectura dirigida y repaso

Las oraciones pueden variar. Damos ejemplos de respuestas.

1. Muchas emisoras de radio y televisión tienen programas en varios idiomas para poder servir a los muchos grupos étnicos.
2. Quieren proteger su herencia, y, en particular, su idioma.
3. En Quebec, las señales de tráfico, los letreros de los calles y los anuncios comerciales están en francés e inglés.
4. Quieren proteger sus culturas y recuperar sus tierras.
5. Los chipewyan demandaron al gobierno por haberles quitado sus tierras; los inuit convencieron al gobierno que les diera terrenos en los Territorios del Noroeste, que se convirtió en un territorio nuevo.
6. En las décadas de los veinte y los treinta, los artistas que se especializaban en pintar paisajes desarrollaron nuevas técnicas para pintar los paisajes canadienses.
7. Algunos de los escritores y músicos famosos de Canadá son Margaret Atwood, Alice Munro y Gordon Lightfoot.
8. Canadá exportó el hockey y el lacrosse a los Estados Unidos.
9. Los equipos estadounidenses y canadienses de hockey compiten por la Copa Stanley.
10. zona separada por el gobierno canadiense para los nativos americanos

Sección 2 Examen

1. c	6. b
2. e	7. d
3. a	8. d
4. d	9. a
5. b	10. b

Actividad de vocabulario

Las oraciones pueden variar. Damos ejemplos de respuestas.

1. b; Existía un intercambio cultural entre los distintos grupos de nativos americanos mucho antes de que llegaran los europeos.
2. c; Cuando los pueblos nativos fueron obligados a vivir en las reservas, perdieron sus tierras ancestrales.
3. d; Canadá es un país bilingüe en el que el inglés y el francés son los dos idiomas oficiales.
4. a; Los miembros de distintos grupos étnicos han contribuido a la cultura de los Estados Unidos.

Capítulo 4

Sección I Lectura dirigida y repaso

1. metro, autobús, taxi, automóvil y transbordador
2. la cadena de ciudades desde Boston a Nueva York y a Washington, D.C.
3. en la ciudades
4. Porque está ubicado cerca de la boca del Río Delaware y porque importantes rutas de transporte terrestres y acuáticas pasan por la ciudad; materias primas de todo el mundo llegan a Filadelfia; miles de fábricas producen mercancía que se exporta en barco.
5. por sus universidades y sus centros tecnológicos
6. Alrededor de 500,000 neoyorquinos trabajan en bancos e instituciones financieras; las oficinas centrales de muchas de las corporaciones más ricas del país y la bolsa de Nueva York se encuentran allí.
7. Ellis Island en Nueva York
8. la rutina diaria de ir y volver del trabajo

Spanish Support

Respuestas

9. región en la que las ciudades y los centros urbanos están tan cerca las unas a las otras que forman juntos una extensa zona urbana
10. número promedio de personas por milla cuadrada o por kilómetro cuadrado

Sección 1 Examen

1. c
2. e
3. a
4. b
5. d
6. c
7. d
8. a
9. c
10. b

Sección 2 Lectura dirigida y repaso

Las oraciones pueden variar. Damos ejemplos de respuestas.

1. Durante muchos años el algodón fue el cultivo más importante.
2. Hoy en día los cultivos más importantes del sur son los cítricos, el arroz, el durazno y algunas nueces.
3. La industria textilera es una de las industrias más importantes del sur.
4. La industria aeroespacial y de alta tecnología son industrias nuevas en el sur.
5. Miami, Florida y Nueva Orleáns, Luisiana son puertos principales.
6. Muchos turistas van al sur para disfrutar del clima templado, de las playas soleadas y de las ciudades históricas.
7. Las olimpiadas de verano de 1996 fueron en Atlanta; hoy en día, Atlanta es un centro de comercio, transporte y comunicaciones.
8. Washington, D.C. es la capital de los Estados Unidos; es hogar de los líderes de la nación y de cientos de diplomáticos extranjeros.
9. petroquímicos
10. el "cinturón soleado"
11. industrialización

Sección 2 Examen

1. V
2. F; Atlanta es en una de las regiones de mayor crecimiento en el sur de los Estados Unidos.
3. F; La industrialización es la transición de una economía basada en la agricultura a una economía basada en la industria.
4. V
5. F; Washington, D.C. está ubicado entre los estados de Maryland y Virginia.
6. b
7. d
8. a
9. c
10. b

Sección 3 Lectura dirigida y repaso

Las oraciones pueden variar. Damos ejemplos de respuestas.

1. Hasta la década de los ochenta, las granjas familiares prosperaron.
2. Una recesión llevó a muchos granjeros a la bancarrota.
3. Grandes corporaciones compraron muchas granjas pequeñas que al unirlas formaron enormes haciendas corporativas.
4. Tantas personas han dejado las granjas que hoy en día la mayoría de la población del medio oeste vive en ciudades.
5. Desde la mitad hasta el final del siglo XIX, Chicago fue un centro de producción alimenticia y de maquinaria agrícola; hoy en día es uno de las ciudades más grandes del medio oeste y un centro cultural y de transporte.
6. Detroit es la sede de la industria automotriz de los Estados Unidos.
7. granja que produce una variedad de cultivos
8. disminución en la actividad comercial
9. granja grande que es manejada por una compañía en vez de una familia

Sección 3 Examen

1. d
2. a
3. c
4. b
5. e
6. c
7. a
8. c
9. b
10. c

Sección 4 Lectura dirigida y repaso

1. el cuidado adecuado
2. recursos naturales
3. población
4. la costa noroeste del Pacífico
5. parques y bosques nacionales
6. ciudades

Respuestas

7. madera, pieles, cereales, salmon, lana
8. el "Valle de la Silicona"
9. los *forty niners*
10. transporte masivo

Sección 4 Examen

1. c	6. a
2. a	7. a
3. d	8. c
4. b	9. c
5. e	10. d

Actividad de vocabulario

Las oraciones pueden variar. Damos ejemplos de respuestas.

1. Muchas personas que trabajan en las ciudades grandes hacen viajes cotidianos desde sus viviendas a sus trabajos.
2. La cadena de ciudades desde Boston a Washington, D.C. forman una megalópolis.
3. La región noroeste de los Estados Unidos tiene la densidad de población más alta del país.
4. Durante los últimos 50 años, la industrialización ha llegado a todas partes del sur.
5. Las pequeñas granjas familiares de los Estados Unidos solían ser haciendas de cultivos mixtos, en caso de que si un cultivo no producía, la granja aún quedaba protegida.
6. A principios de los años ochenta, muchos granjeros fueron obligados a vender sus granjas a causa de la recesión.
7. Durante la recesión, muchas granjas familiares fueron compradas por compañías que las unieron para formar grandes haciendas corporativas.
8. El método que usaban los *forty niners* para minar oro consitía en lavar trozos pequeños de oro de las corrientes de agua.
9. Si más personas usaran el transporte masivo en vez del automóvil, podríamos reducir la contaminación ambiental.

Capítulo 5

Sección 1 Lectura dirigida y repaso

1. El río Ottawa
2. En Ontario se habla inglés; en Quebec se habla francés.
3. Después de la Segunda Guerra Mundial, muchos inmigrantes europeos se asentaron en Toronto, y en fechas recientes Toronto ha visto muchos inmigrantes de Hong Kong y China.
4. Jacques Cartier reclamó la región para Francia en el siglo XVI y muchos colonos franceses se quedaron en la región después de que Inglaterra se apoderó de Quebec en 1763.
5. Los separatistas en Quebec esperan que Quebec puede separarse del Canadá y convertirse en país independiente.
6. francófonos
7. separatista
8. autónomo
9. escudo canadiense
10. revolución pacífica
11. federación
12. los plebiscitos

Sección 1 Examen

1. F; La ciudad capital del Canadá es Ottawa.
2. V
3. V
4. F; Jacques Cartier desembarcó en Stadacona y declaró que la región pertenecía a Francia.
5. V
6. b
7. d
8. c
9. a
10. d

Sección 2 Lectura dirigida y repaso

1. Manitoba, Saskatchewan y Alberta se encuentran en la pradera más extensa del mundo.
2. Estas provincias son las más recientes del Dominio del Canadá.
3. Los pueblos cree, salteaux, blackfoot, assiniboine y chipewyan se contaron entre los pueblos nativos de las llanuras.

Spanish Support

Respuestas

4. Los pueblos nativos dependían del búfalo para sobrevivir.

5. Las personas de ascendencia europea mataron casi todos los búfalo.

6. Las enfermedades de los europeos mataron muchos pueblos indígenas.

7. Muchos inmigrantes europeos vinieron en busca de la promesa de tierras gratuitas y se convirtieron en agricultores canadienses.

8. El gobierno canadiense se apoderó de los terrenos de los pueblos nativos.

9. En las provincias de la pradera se celebran en festivales las diferentes culturas y orígenes étnicos de la región.

10. El trigo es el cultivo más importante de "la despensa del Canadá" y se celebra en eventos como el festival del trigo de Weyburn.

11. serie de antecesores de una persona

12. resistencia natural a una enfermedad

Sección 2 Examen

1. c   **2.** a   **3.** b   **4.** e   **5.** d
6. b   **7.** c   **8.** a   **9.** d   **10.** d

Sección 3 Lectura dirigida y repaso

1. costumbres
2. comerciar
3. oro
4. mineros
5. colonias prósperas
6. los costumbres, las religiones, los idiomas
7. derechos
8. ferrocarril
9. las naciones de la costa del Pacífico
10. Asia
11. tótem
12. colonia próspera

Sección 3 Examen

1. e   **2.** a   **3.** b   **4.** d   **5.** c
6. b   **7.** d   **8.** a   **9.** c   **10.** a

Actividad de vocabulario

Las oraciones pueden variar. Damos ejemplos de respuestas.

1. e; En un plebiscito en Quebec en 1980, los ciudadanos decidieron si Quebec debería ser una nación independiente.

2. i; Algunos de los pueblos nativos del Canadá pensaban que la aurora borealis eran espíritus.

3. d; Después de "la revolución pacífica", el nuevo gobierno declaró al francés el idioma oficial de la provincia.

4. f; Los separatistas de Quebec formaron un partido político que tomó el control de la legislatura en 1976.

5. g; Si visitas una aldea tradicional de los pueblos nativos en el noroeste de la costa del Pacífico, es muy probable que veas un tótem.

6. b; Los francoparlantes forman la mayoría de la población de Quebec.

7. a; Durante la fiebre de oro de Canadá, las colonias prósperas crecieron rápidamente.

8. h; Las actividades marítimas son el enfoque de la vida en las provincias del Atlántico.

9. c; Los pueblos nativos de América del Norte no tenían inmunidad a enfermedades europeas, como el sarampión.

Sección 4 Lectura dirigida y repaso

1. Terranova, Prince Edward Island, Nueva Brunswick, Nova Scotia

2. Las provincias del Atlántico se encuentran a lo largo del Océano Atlántico en el oriente canadiense, y la mayoría de sus habitantes viven en la costa.

3. Cuando los ingleses se apoderaron de Acadia en 1755, ellos temían que los residentes de ascendencia francesa guardaran lealtades secretas hacia Francia.

4. La economía de las provincias del Atlántico depende de actividades marítimas tales como la pesca y la construcción de buques (astilleros).

5. Se comenzó a construir muchos buques de acero, lo que desaceleró la economía de las provincias que hasta entonces había dependido de la silvicultura.

Respuestas

6. Miles de residentes de las provincias del Atlántico trabajan en la industria de la pesca, y alrededor del 75 por ciento del pescado del Canadá proviene de esta región.

7. Se perdieron millones de dólares y los habitantes de la provincia cambiaron su enfoque hacia otros tipos de pescado.

8. El procesamiento del pescado (congelarlo, salarlo, ahumarlo y enlatarlo) y la acuacultura (el cultivo de peces y plantas acuáticas) son dos industrias en auge en las provincias del Atlántico.

9. exiliaron

10. marítima

11. acuacultura

Sección 4 Examen

1. V
2. V
3. F; Construir buques (los astilleros) es un ejemplo de una industria marítima.
4. V
5. F; Cuando alguien está exilado de un sitio quiere decir que está obligado a irse de allí permanentemente.

6. d   7. b   8. c   9. b   10. a

Sección 5 Lectura dirigida y repaso

1. Los Territorios del Noroeste, el Yukón y Nunavut comprenden más de una tercera parte de la extensión total del Canadá.

2. La región es más que todo tundra y muy accidentada.

3. Menos del uno por ciento de la población del Canadá vive en esta región.

4. Casi la mitad de la población está compuesta por pueblos nativos.

5. Los territorios tienen representación en el Parlamento canadiense.

6. El gobierno federal tiene más control sobre los territorios que sobre las provincias.

7. Durante la fiebre del oro del Klondike, casi 30,000 personas llegaron al territorio del Yukon.

8. Para 1898 casi todas estas personas habían abandonado la región.

9. Nunavut, habitado más que todo por el pueblo inuit, fue convertido en territorio canadiense en 1999.

10. Debido a ser región remota y de clima inhóspito, será un verdadero desafío mantener fuerte la economía.

11. las luces norteñas

Sección 4 Examen

1. c   2. a   3. d   4. b   5. e
6. b   7. a   8. d   9. d   10. c